CODEX ALIMENTARIUS
GLOBAL FOOD IMPERIALISM

A Compendium of Articles on Codex
Edited by Scott C. Tips

FHR

Foundation For Health Research
Monrovia, California
USA

Publisher: Foundation for Health Research
Editor: Scott C. Tips
Assistant Editors: Tamara Thérèsa Mosegaard, Cheri L. Tips
Graphic Designer: Erin L. Murphy

Foundation for Health Research
P.O. Box 688
Monrovia, California 91017
1-626-357-2181

FIRST EDITION

ISBN 978-0-9795670-0-1

Printed in the United States of America

This book is dedicated to the memory of
Maureen Kennedy Salaman (1936-2006) and to the countless
thousands of other health-freedom fighters throughout the
World who have fought the hard and often thankless
fight for true health and liberty.

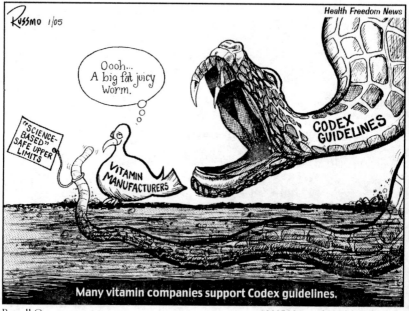

CONTENTS

Foreword by Scott C. Tips i
Codex Organizational Chart x
Introduction by Maureen Kennedy Salaman xi

Part I (1994-1999)
Comments Regarding the Proposal of the German Federal 1
Health Office (BGA) for a Codex Alimentarius Draft Regulation
Regarding Food Supplements - Vitamins and Minerals
By Sepp Hasslberger

Despite Victory Over One Codex Proposal The Need 9
Remains for Further Activism
By John C. Hammell

The Codex Alimentarius Commission 15
By Tamara Thérèsa Mosegaard

The Codex Alimentarius Information 17
An Introduction
By Alex Dybring & Tamara Thérèsa Mosegaard

Part II (2000-2005)
Codex to Meet Again: Health Freedom at Risk 21
By Scott C. Tips

MayDay as Observer of Codex Alimentarius 25
By Tamara Thérèsa Mosegaard,

Breathe Easier - Codex Adjourns 31
By Scott C. Tips

International Law Trumps Domestic Law 37
By Scott C. Tips

Comments on My Trip to Codex 41
By Susan Negus, Ph.D

Codex Gets One Step Closer To Control 47
By Scott C. Tips

AHHA Attends Berlin Codex Session. What Did We Learn? 55
By Suzan Walter

Who Decides About Our Health? 65
Baby Foods, Nutritional Supplements, and "Codex Alimentarius"
By Sepp Hasslberger

Report From The Eastern Front: 73
Author finds much to mistrust at recent Codex session in Berlin
By Scott C. Tips

Rearranging The Deck Chairs On The Titanic 79
By Scott C. Tips

Important News from Bonn 85
By Suzan Walter

A Meeting Of Two 95
By Scott C. Tips

South Africa Opposes Codex Rule on 105
Food Health Information
By Sepp Hasslberger

Codex - The Root of the Problem Identified 109
By Paul Anthony Taylor

Codex Guidelines for Vitamin and Mineral Supplements: 119
The Controversy Continues
By Paul Anthony Taylor

Codex Nutrition Committee: Supplement Guidelines Final 127
By Sepp Hasslberger

Codex: WHO/FAO Told Nutrient Risk 131
Assessment Must Consider Benefits
By Sepp Hasslberger

Looks Like the EU Outmaneuvered the U.S. 137
By Suzan Walter

Codex Guidelines History (1987-2004) 143
By Suzan Walter

Summer of '05: 155
Critical Time for Dietary Supplements
By Suzan Walter

The Summer Of Our Discontent: How the Codex Commission 161
Lost Its Rulebook and the European Court of Justice Found Its Own
By Scott C. Tips

The Worst Is Still To Come 171
By Paul Anthony Taylor

Codex Committee in Germany Weighs Vitamin Restrictions ... 179
By Sepp Hasslberger

Shangri-La On The Rhine 183
The Codex Committee Meets Again in Bonn
By Scott C. Tips

Part III (2006-Present)

Codex Committee For Food Labeling 191
By Scott C. Tips

Report from the Thai Codex Meeting 197
By Ingrid Franzon

When It Comes to GM Food, Some Say Ignorance is Bliss 203
By Tamara Thérèsa Mosegaard & Scott C. Tips

North American Union: 209
FDA's Trilateral Cooperation Charter With Canada & Mexico
Threatens to Scuttle Consumer Access to Dietary Supplements
By John C. Hammell

The Maginot Mentality 217
By Scott C. Tips

About The Authors 227
Appendices 234

FOREWORD

CODEX ALIMENTARIUS – GLOBAL FOOD IMPERIALISM

WHAT IS Codex?

As is often the case with governmental programs and the ostensibly good intentions that are professed to accompany them, the implementation of those programs and the resulting effects upon the individuals affected by them are invariably negative. Whether it has been the American government's 35-plus-year-old failed "War on Cancer" or its equally-long and equally unsuccessful "War on Drugs," for example, each massive increase in taxpayer money thrown at the problem by the government has not resulted in a cure or solution but simply more bureaucracy, more tunnel-vision as to the path to take, and an ever-receding goal still stretching out of reach.

It is perhaps the prime example of the "Law of Unintended Consequences." This law of nature (which says that an action or program will have the opposite or at least unexpected effect of that intended) seems to dog government actions no matter what they are. And Codex Alimentarius, an international intergovernmental program, enjoys no special exemption from this Law.

Codex Alimentarius is actually a noble concept. The idea – at least the idea put forth to the public – has been for countries throughout the World to adopt uniform food standards that would allow the free and unhindered flow of food goods among countries and to consumers. This is an idea with which many of us can agree and even embrace. But, as you will read in this book, the actual implementation of this laudable ideal is falling far short of the ideal itself. Indeed, the implementation of this ideal is having the *opposite* effect of its stated purpose.

The Food Code

Codex Alimentarius is Latin for "Food Code." It is, and is to be (since the process is still ongoing), a set of standards covering many different categories of food. The Codex Alimentarius Commission is the international body establishing these global trade standards for foods. Created in 1963 as a result of resolutions passed in 1961 at a Food and Agriculture Organization (FAO) conference, and now sponsored jointly by the World Health Organization (WHO) and the FAO of the United Nations, Codex has some 27 active committees dealing with various food and food-labeling issues from fish and infant-feeding formulas to food additives and vegetable proteins. And each committee is hosted in turn by a particular country that provides both the chairman and the meeting place in that country.

The stated goal of the Commission is to promote and protect the health of the public. This follows from the FAO's own stated purpose of "achieving food security for all" and its desire "to make sure people have regular access to enough high quality food to lead active, healthy lives." With the establishment of the World Trade Organization (WTO) in 1995, and the subsequent institution of various trade and other agreements, an additional goal of removing barriers to trade has also emerged.

CCNFSDU

The committee concerned with food supplements is the one with the annoyingly long acronym: the Codex Committee on Nutrition and Foods for Special Dietary Uses (CCNFSDU), which is hosted and chaired by Germany. Typically, the CCNFSDU meets in Bonn, or near Bonn, every November, although the committee meeting in October-November 2006 took place in Chiang Mai, Thailand in deference to Third World sensibilities.

As its name implies, the CCNFSDU covers a number of agenda items in its meetings, including the ever-controversial infant formula standards, dietary fiber guidelines, proposals for nutrient-content claims, and risk analysis. The CCNFSDU chairman is Dr. Rolf Grossklaus, a German functionary who wields considerable control over the proceedings and who only occasionally faces revolts from the delegate attendees and only then if he has been particularly high-handed.

The delegates to these committee meetings are themselves

almost universally regulatory bureaucrats and functionaries themselves, largely out of touch with the interests of the consumers they purport to represent. The United States delegation, for example, consists of the U.S. Representative, a Food and Drug Administration (FDA) employee, and her assistant delegate, yet another FDA employee, as well as a smattering of special-interest industry persons who may or may not be listened to by the FDA delegate, depending upon whose interests they represent. To make sure that these private individuals who plump up the U.S. Delegation are properly hamstrung, the FDA requires as a condition of their attendance that they sign a form promising that they will not lobby other countries' Codex delegates at these meetings.

For two years, I myself was a member of the U.S. Delegation attending the CCNFSDU meetings in Berlin, Germany. I found that the views I expressed on behalf of the National Health Federation (NHF), a nonprofit health-freedom organization representing the views of thousands of pro-supplement and pro-health individuals, mostly fell on very deaf ears.

It was not until 2002, when the then-U.S. delegate, Dr. Elizabeth Yetley, refused to let me continue being on the delegation that I was spurred into action to obtain official Codex-recognized status for the NHF as an International Non-Governmental Organization (INGO) and could then attend and speak out at the CCNFSDU and other Codex meetings unfettered by FDA handcuffs. Indeed, it is really thanks to Dr. Yetley's refusal, which completely backfired, that the NHF could begin to have an impact at the Codex meetings. Often, in speaking out at the meetings, the NHF has taken a position opposite to that of the United States, which U.S. position the NHF has found to be antithetical to the very principles of freedom upon which the United States was founded.

The Guidelines

Despite the often-fierce First World-versus-Third World battle over infant formulas, this particular committee achieved even more notoriety and thus the object of focus for health-freedom activists around the World in 1994 when it took up more directly the issue of vitamin-and-mineral food supplements. In doing so, it began establishing "guidelines" intended to govern the international trade in vitamins and minerals.

Interestingly enough, these Codex *Guidelines for Vitamin and Mineral Food Supplements* are intended to apply only to those jurisdictions (read, countries) where supplements are regulated as foods. Where they are regulated instead as drugs, such as in supplement-hating Norway, these *Guidelines* are more of a curiosity than something of importance. So, the game has been rigged almost from the beginning. In a bureaucratic form of "heads I win, tails you lose," the *Guidelines* will clamp down on both the quality and availability of supplements being sold as food while having no effect on those supplements legally classified as drugs.

The NHF – along with the freedom-loving South African delegate, Antoinette Booyzen – fought hard to prevent or at least slow down the establishment of the recently-adopted *Guidelines for Vitamin and Mineral Food Supplements*. Obviously modeled after the European Union's Food Supplements directive of 2002, these *Guidelines* take an anti-health-freedom, bureaucrat-friendly approach to natural substances that purports to protect health and lives through severe restrictions upon the sale and information given about vitamins and minerals. Yet, by making health-saving information about vitamins and minerals virtually impossible to obtain and by limiting consumer access to health-benefiting vitamins and minerals at levels that will actually make a physiological difference, these arguably well-intentioned regulators are ensuring the ill-health of future generations.

Used to a toxicological model of dealing with substances they know little about and, hence, mistrust, these Codex bureaucrats are painting everything in their path with a very wide brush and the same color paint. Again, the Law of Unintended Consequences is at work here.

In November 2004, at the Bonn, Germany CCNFSDU meeting, South Africa and the National Health Federation were the only delegations opposing approval by the Committee of these harsh *Guidelines*. According to Codex procedural rules, the *Guidelines* were then required to be submitted to the next regular meeting of the Codex Alimentarius Commission for final review and approval. So it was, then, that at the July 2005 Codex Alimentarius Commission meeting in Rome, Italy (and with Mrs. Booyzen absent), the NHF was the one and only voice – out of literally hundreds of attendees – to speak up and oppose the Commission's adoption of the *Guidelines*.

It is important to remember, though, that at present these *Guidelines* are nothing more than a framework, with maximum permitted upper levels for vitamins and minerals to be slotted in under a risk-assessment approach. Ever fearful of vitamins and minerals, which they have never understood, the Europeans are striving to keep a firm lid on the maximum permitted upper levels. And, unfortunately, instead of opposing this straightjacket, the Americans, Canadians, and many others are willing – even eager – midwives to the process.

While the birthing process still has a few years to go, in the regulatory timescale, this is the merest blink of an eye. To us, bureaucrats move glacially slow; but in their strange Einsteinian universe the few years left to complete and fill in the Guidelines' framework is a heart-pounding rocket-ride to the stars.

Harmonization

What many health-freedom activists around the World have long ago realized, however, is that these euphemistically called "guidelines" will be used not only to exclude high-potency American dietary supplements from the European marketplace but they will also be used, either directly or by way of example, to stifle the *domestic* national markets in supplements as well through a leveling process called "harmonization."

Importantly, though, harmonization of food standards is not just a Codex process but is a deliberately-planned interlocking process being fitted together through a number of treaties, "agreements," and regulatory "handshakes" that, once in place, will make it nearly impossible for any countries' citizens to shake themselves free of this straightjacket. These harmonization processes include, but are not limited to, the World Trade Organization, the Sanitary and PhytoSanitary (SPS) agreements, the Technical Barriers to Trade (TBT) agreement, the North American Free Trade Agreement (NAFTA), the Central American Free Trade Agreement (CAFTA), the Trilateral Cooperation Charter, and the planned North American Union (NAU).

And if any of you are still under the illusion that any government, but especially the American government, is a supporter of health freedom or a protector of health-freedom rights in any way, then you need only look to the actions and words of the FDA. This

Agency has not only announced its intention to harmonize U.S. laws and regulations to international standards but it has been acting upon the World stage for years to do just that. It does not matter to the FDA that the Dietary Supplement Health and Education Act of 1994 (DSHEA) was passed by Congress in order to protect certain of the health freedoms of Americans. The FDA has always hated this law, which removed FDA's arbitrary enforcement powers (but not, as is often claimed, its regulatory powers), and has seen that although it cannot yet directly repeal DSHEA, it can and will outflank DSHEA through harmonization with anti-freedom rules, regulations, and "guidelines."

It is not the purpose of this Foreword to explain how this process of harmonization will affect the North American and other global markets in general and dietary supplements in particular, but rather through the following collection of articles gathered together and presented to you in this compilation – written as they were by many of those individuals who have monitored, argued, and written about Codex over numerous years – you will more completely grasp what many have realized and argued is nothing more than a net slowly descending over our collective heads to benefit a few.

Many have claimed that somewhere along the way Codex was hijacked by financial interests antithetical to the true health interests of consumers. Using propagandistic phrases such as "the need to protect consumer health," these commercial interests have allied themselves with the naturally future-fearing tendencies of government bureaucrats to suppress the rapidly rising use of dietary supplements. What better way to eliminate the competition than to suppress it with regulatory and legislative handcuffs? The pharmaceutical industry, with a global market of more than $600 billion, will act, and has been acting, to protect it's commercial interests.

The Players

As will be evident from reading this collection of articles and essays, there are many players in this drama. While Sepp Hasslberger, a Bavarian living in Rome, Italy, was probably the first to privately call attention to the Codex threat, and while the National Health Federation began following Codex from afar in 1995-1996, it was John Hammell of the International Advocates of Health Freedom (IAHF) – to my knowledge – who *first* publicly pulled the alarm bell on Codex in 1996 with his very first article on the subject, republished here in this book.

Around the same time, Suzanne Harris, a Kansas-City based journalist with degrees in law and political science, began reporting on international Codex meetings at the suggestion of the NHF and with partial funding from the NHF. Her investigations and articles also helped educate many of us to developing events at Codex.

As did Dr. Mathias Rath and his Foundation, which had not only been monitoring Codex meetings but actively demonstrating against them as well with large crowds, big signs, and speaking events. While I did not think his demonstrations were effective, Dr. Rath, to his credit, has poured much of his own personal money into fighting Codex restrictions on vitamins and minerals.

Then, in early 2000, with much of my time spent in Europe, I suggested to NHF president Maureen Kennedy Salaman that NHF start sending me to the CCNFSDU meetings in Berlin. Not hesitating even a second, she agreed and the path for the Federation to start regularly attending what up to then it had only been monitoring and reporting on was established. In June 2000, I attended my first Codex meeting and wrote a report – found here – on what transpired. Coincidentally, and although I did not meet them at this Codex meeting, both Sepp Hasslberger of LaLeva and Tamara Thèrésa Mosegaard of MayDay also attended this Codex meeting for the first time as members of their respective countries' delegations.

The following year's meeting in Berlin (with the meeting dates then changed to the Fall) saw the beginning of the involvement of the American Holistic Health Association (AHHA), with both Susan Negus and Suzan Walter attending several Codex meetings and reporting their own observations and conclusions.

Many others have since been inspired to become more familiar with and involved in Codex work. These include Paul Anthony Taylor of both NHF and the Rath Foundation (who began attending Codex meetings in 2003), Diane Miller of the National Health Freedom Coalition, Carolyn Dean of Friends of Freedom International, Brenna Hill of the American Association for Health Freedom, and, more recently, Robert Verkerk of the Alliance for Natural Health. The absence of others, unnamed here, is not intended to slight them in any way, but will probably be more a reflection of my memory, or lack thereof.

Importantly, award-winning film-maker Kevin Miller researched wrote, filmed, and produced an excellent documentary on Codex Alimentarius called *We Become Silent* that features some of the individuals mentioned above and presents much information on Codex in an educational and entertaining way. Oscar-winning actress Dame Judi Dench narrates the film.

At the same time, the other players in this Codex drama include the CCNFSDU chairman Dr. Rolf Grossklaus, the EU/EC Codex representative Basil Mathioudakis, Dr. Elizabeth Yetley and her successor, Dr. Barbara Schneeman, as the U.S./FDA delegates, Dr. John Hathcock of the Council for Responsible Nutrition, James Turner and James Gormley of Citizens for Health, and the International Alliance of Dietary Food Supplement Associations. Often at crossed swords with the writers in this book, these individuals and organizations have figured large at Codex meetings or otherwise participated in some way.

Last, but certainly not least, a very important player at Codex meetings has been Antoinette Booyzen, the South African delegate. It was Mrs. Booyzen who, courageously and usually alone among national delegations (although supported by NHF), stood up and faced the ire and even ridicule of the Chairman and many others for daring to speak out for the right of all persons to exercise their right to consume healthy, nourishing foods and supplements. Her undaunted courage at these meetings was an inspiringly frequent occurrence.

What the Future Holds

Although the Codex Alimentarius Commission has adopted the *Guidelines*, there are still two arenas in which this health-freedom drama will play out. These are the two areas that bear the most watching.

First, since the *Guidelines* are nothing more than a framework, they are not useable until the maximum permitted levels are established through the application of risk analysis and risk assessment. So, the fight here will be over how high the vitamin-and-mineral potencies will be set, with the pro-health-freedom forces agitating for the highest possible levels and the pro-pharmaceutical interests wanting to minimize the upper levels (and hence the effectiveness) as much as possible. The science is on the side of the proponents of health freedom, but the "beauty" of science merged with politics is that it can be easily manipulated to say whatever its manipulators want it to say. The future will tell us whether truth and scientific integrity prevail or whether politics as usual will rule.

The second arena will be the application of the Guidelines domestically within each country's national boundaries, otherwise known as "harmonization." Already, countries are lining up like lemmings to accept whatever cliff-edge Codex standards would have them jump off of.

As in the case of the development of Codex standards, harmonization is not simply a process, it has actually become a way of thinking. Numerous countries, institutions, and individuals have come to accept harmonization as inevitable. In a sort of "Borg-like, resistance is futile" fog of mind, they have ceased to question the value of harmonization, or to compare the advantages with the disadvantages, or especially to consider that there might be a far better way to handle the health issues presented to them.

It has been often said that to know the future one should remember the past. It is for this reason that the Foundation for Health Research has – with the kind permission of the authors whose works appear herein – compiled and published the ensuing collection of articles in one place so that you, the reader, may see and follow the historical progression of thought on this important Codex issue, an issue that will profoundly affect everyone's health in the years to come.

- Scott C. Tips
President, Foundation for Health Research
April 4, 2007, the European Union

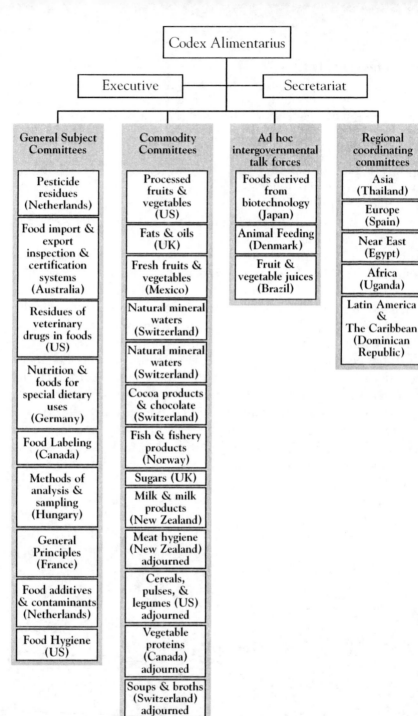

Codex Alimentarius

Executive — **Secretariat**

General Subject Committees

- Pesticide residues (Netherlands)
- Food import & export inspection & certification systems (Australia)
- Residues of veterinary drugs in foods (US)
- Nutrition & foods for special dietary uses (Germany)
- Food Labeling (Canada)
- Methods of analysis & sampling (Hungary)
- General Principles (France)
- Food additives & contaminants (Netherlands)
- Food Hygiene (US)

Commodity Committees

- Processed fruits & vegetables (US)
- Fats & oils (UK)
- Fresh fruits & vegetables (Mexico)
- Natural mineral waters (Switzerland)
- Natural mineral waters (Switzerland)
- Cocoa products & chocolate (Switzerland)
- Fish & fishery products (Norway)
- Sugars (UK)
- Milk & milk products (New Zealand)
- Meat hygiene (New Zealand) adjourned
- Cereals, pulses, & legumes (US) adjourned
- Vegetable proteins (Canada) adjourned
- Soups & broths (Switzerland) adjourned

Ad hoc intergovernmental talk forces

- Foods derived from biotechnology (Japan)
- Animal Feeding (Denmark)
- Fruit & vegetable juices (Brazil)

Regional coordinating committees

- Asia (Thailand)
- Europe (Spain)
- Near East (Egypt)
- Africa (Uganda)
- Latin America & The Caribbean (Dominican Republic)

INTRODUCTION

CODEX ALIMENTARIUS –
International Threat To Our Health Freedoms

*God grant, that not only the Love of Liberty, but a
thorough Knowledge of the Rights of Man, may pervade all the
Nations of the Earth, so that a Philosopher may set his foot any-
where on its Surface, and say, "This is my Country."*
-- *Benjamin Franklin*

As you observe the abundance of nutritional supplements in your local health-food store or supermarket, deciding which to purchase and what to take; as you exercise your freedom to keep yourself healthy and prevent illness and disease, realize that your rights are insidiously being chipped away by a tyrannical tribunal of global elitists.

Beware the future, as agents implement their plan to wreck the dietary-supplement industry so the world can be made safe for toxic, deadly synthetic chemicals. They are advancing with great speed as the machinations of the UN-aligned Codex Alimentarius Commission brings supplements and related products under the control of Big Pharma, and its collaborating government machinery.

Who Are These People?

Codex Alimentarius is a set of international trade standards for food quality and safety established to "protect the health of consumers and ensure fair practices in the food trade." In classic 1984 Orwellian newspeak, that's what they want us to believe.

The Codex Commission and its many committees were established by, and work in coordination with, the Food and Agriculture Organization of the United Nations (FAO) and the World Health Organization (WHO) - since 1963.

One of the assignments of one of those committees, the Codex Committee on Nutrition and Foods for Special Dietary Uses (CCN FSDU), was to formulate "Guidelines for Vitamin and Mineral Food Supplements." These guidelines dictate which nutrients are deemed safe, the maximum and minimum amounts allowed in a product, and certain packaging and labeling standards.

The delegates that formulate the Codex mandates are government employees, bureaucrats and functionaries, most of whom seem to be greatly indebted to, counseled by, and/or strongly influenced by the giant multi-national pharmaceutical corporations - the drug companies who want to monopolize and create pharmaceutical versions of the natural health-food and supplement manufacturing industries of the World.

What Are They Doing To Our Rights?

Sponsored and/or strongly influenced by international pharmaceutical interests, the Codex Commission intends to circumvent the U.S. and other governments and their people, and bring about a prohibition on nutritional supplements of any reasonable potency and hence value.

An example of the consequences: possession of DHEA is now a felony in Canada with the same penalty as that for the possession of drugs. You could go to jail simply for having DHEA in your house. One-gram Vitamin C tablets are hard to find now, and soon they will become available by prescription only, once Big Pharma can do as it pleases with the police power that will be put into place courtesy of standards being developed by the Codex Alimentarius Commission.

The pharmaceutical model calls for an end to the use of dietary supplements for preventative use, the adoption of strict potency limits set by Codex for implementation in all member countries, and Codex approval of all dietary supplements. In other words, the bloody carnage that takes place when the fox guards the hen house.

What this really means is that supplements will be controlled as if they were drugs. Prescription control of natural nutrients means only one thing: their removal from the marketplace where they pose a huge economic challenge to the pharmaceutical drug pushers. The name of the game is to not allow any supplements that would be useful over and above the "food-physiological" handling of deficiencies.

A typical sentiment erupted from the mouth of a Columbian delegate at the 2005 Codex Commission meeting in Rome, Italy: "Vitamins are dangerous and should be stopped!"

Ignorance is certainly more dangerous.

The Cost of Ignorance

Typical Recommended Daily Allowances (RDAs) are inadequate, and are of no benefit to your health. Limiting the amount of nutrients a supplement can contain not only effectively prohibits its therapeutic use, but drives prices up to equal the stratospheric cost of pharmaceuticals. This rise equates to the 7,000 percent mark up on drugs that is currently crippling so many of our industries.

Two of our biggest industries are the automobile and airline industries. Both are now facing bankruptcy. To learn why, you only have to do a cost comparison. For every car manufactured, General Motors pays $500 for the metal and $1,500 for workers' medical costs. In a monopoly, you have high cost and low-quality goods. In a free-market system, you have the best product for the lowest cost.

Within the next five years medical costs will exceed the Gross National Product, yet the noose of medical monopoly continues to be drawn more tightly around our necks.

A valid concern is that Codex will gain political and economic leverage to restrict U.S. and World consumers' personal access to dietary supplements. With the *Codex Guidelines* currently matching – or slated to match – closely the European Food Supplements Directive, lawful sales into Europe of the high-value, low-cost, usually superior American dietary supplements will be prevented.

As long as we are not free to choose what we put into our mouths to keep us healthy, overcome illness and save our lives, we are not free. We are the slaves of an omnipotent State.

We must wake our fellow Americans up to George Washington's admonitions, which resounds down through the generations: "Government is not reason. It is not eloquence. It is force. Like fire, it is a dangerous servant and a fearful master." Our forefather's assessment must ring today in the hearts of every American and, indeed, every other free man and woman if we are to remain free.

The greatest deterrent to knowledge is the illusion of knowledge. The World establishment is giving false information in order to influence others against supplements, taking away your rights and freedoms with lies and falsehoods.

The Codex Commission and its committees embrace politics, self-interest, and fear so as to undermine the value of nutritional supplements, choosing to reject valid science that proves the life-saving merit of higher doses and our rights to use them as such, and instead embracing wholly inaccurate arguments that use junk science.

Join Us in The Fight

As self-serving interests attempted to influence international laws and regulations to restrict access to beneficial supplements, only the National Health Federation (NHF), the largest and oldest health-freedom organization in the World, has been consistently there at the meetings to try to stop them.

Attorney Scott Tips of the National Health Federation has been there to lead the charge against these unreasonable Codex restrictions. For a long time he was a courageous, lone voice in a sea of ignorance and misinformation as he exposed the deceptions, closed the loopholes and unsheathed the false science, eventually bringing others aboard and shining the bright light of sweet reason onto the proceedings.

The Bible says, "My people perish for lack of vision." Visionless living leads to diminished living, in this case. A loss of vision leads to loss of life. Take what you have learned here and deliver the roar. With the heart of a lion we stretch ourselves and make a difference in our World. Ghandi once said, "You must be the change you want to see in the World." You are the World, now change it!

Don't fall into discouragement by thinking your letters, e-mails, faxes, and personal visits don't make a difference. While lobbying for our health freedoms in Washington, D.C., I check the government mailrooms. If a legislator gets three to seven letters a day on one topic, it strongly impacts the legislation. Send your correspondence to the NHF and we will see to it that it goes to your Representative or other government legislator.

For a small donation each year, you will receive a quarterly journal and be a part of the oldest and most effective health-freedom organization in the world. Help us defray the cost of having Scott

Tips and others at every Codex meeting plus a full-time lobbyist that NHF maintains in Washington, D.C. Nothing else will take you further or makes such a lasting impact on your life, liberty and future of your loved ones.

Freedom is all of our responsibility, and the price remains eternal vigilance. Support your freedom by becoming a member of the NHF or making a donation to help us defray the cost of mounting a defense against the Codex guidelines. Nothing else will take your dollars further or make such a lasting impact on your life, your liberty, and the future of your loved ones.

-Maureen Kennedy Salaman
President, National Health Federation
September 2005, Atherton, California

Learn more at the National Health Federation website: www.thenhf.com.

Or contact:

The National Health Federation
P.O. Box 688
Monrovia, California 91017 USA
Phone: 1 (626) 357-2181
Fax: 1 (626) 303-0642
contact-us@thenhf.com

Part I

(1994-1999)

Comments Regarding the Proposal of the German Federal Health Office (BGA) for a Codex Alimentarius Draft Regulation Regarding Food Supplements - Vitamins and Minerals

By Sepp Hasslberger

(submitted 1994, first published 1999)

The proposal of the federal health office (BGA) regarding the area of food supplements does not propose a specific set of guidelines, referring to a future "discussion of basic principles." But it is obvious from the overall tendency of the draft that the (European) citizen is not considered mature enough to take care of his own health with a sensible practice of supplementing his diet and in accordance with the latest research results in the area of preventive nutrition. However it is just this attitude, which signifies an obsessive bureaucratic control without sense or reason, that must be held largely responsible for the current disastrous situation in the area of public health.

If on the one hand, we have to say that the citizen has practically no protection against atmospheric, electromagnetic, and acoustic pollution of his environment (it should probably be a duty of the BGA to provide for such protection), then it is obvious on the other hand that an attempt is being made to use legislative authority in order to deprive the citizen of one of the last remaining tools of biological "self-defense."

Our drinking water in many places has become a quite unpalatable liquid. The relevant levels of maximum allowed pollution are changed as and when needed. In any case, most families have taken to filtering the tap water or have started using only mineral water.

Our foods are impoverished by chemical "fertilizers," and the use of hormones and poisons for weed and pest control as well as industrial processing has left them little more than worthless. True, it is possible, with clever combination of foods, to avoid outright deficiency diseases; but an optimal nutrition (for real health and strong immunity) cannot any longer be achieved by just eating normal foods.

Our environment has come to be a general health risk through a technology and industry which are oriented towards fossil fuels and chemical poisons. Medicine based on pharmaceuticals and expensive apparatus has failed miserably in controlling chronic illness and our immune system is under constant attack not only from environmental pollutants but from such "medicogenic" poisons as vaccines and antibiotics applied without limiting criteria.

In view of these facts, it must be seen as the maximum of bureaucratic obtuseness if now the people are "to be protected against the undesired effects of food supplements." In many cases, it is just those vitamins and minerals and other nutritional substances which allow the individual to "keep afloat" despite continual attacks on his health.

After this admittedly somewhat polemic introduction, which seems necessary to put the discussion in the right perspective, we shall now examine the single parts of the BGA's proposal.

Definitions

It has been correctly pointed out that foods are consumed mainly because of their nutrient content, as well as for purposes of nutrition and taste and that the borderline between foods and medicines is determined by the purpose of the product.

This already shows clearly that a food supplement, regardless of its content of nutrients, has to be considered a food and not a medicine, as long as it is not offered with medical indications. Therefore, discussing a limitation of dosages, as least towards a maximum dosage, seems to be quite superfluous.

The definition of the term "medicine" as a product which serves to diagnose, heal, alleviate, treat, and prevent illnesses and disturbances of body and spirit, and/or which serves to change the build and the function of body and spirit and which is sold for this purpose is in accordance with EC regulations (65/65), but we shall examine this is a bit more closely.

First we have to note that this definition has been made very ample with the purpose of including all traditional medicinal remedies. However, it was not made in order to work out a distinction between foods and medicines. Thus, the attributes of a medicine as listed in the definition must not be seen as exclusive attributes of medicinal products.

In other words, we cannot hold against a food the fact that it may serve to "prevent illnesses or disturbances of body or spirit" or to "change the build or function of body and spirit." For thousands of years, these functions have been fulfilled by both medicines and foods, in many cases mainly by foods. Historically, medicines were used mainly for healing and treatment of illnesses, while prevention was seen as a question of one's lifestyle, and mainly as a question of healthy nutrition.

If we look more closely at the above definition of a medicinal product, another important point strikes the eye: In order for a product to be considered medicinal, the mere function of the product is not enough. A second condition must be fulfilled. The product must also be offered as a medicine. We see this clearly expressed in the words ". . . and which is sold for this purpose."

Of course we cannot presume to put a chemical pharmaceutical substance on free sale, using this argumentation. But when we are dealing with substances that are normally consumed with foods, even if these substances are offered in higher concentration, then these are not to be considered medicines only because that have also been sold as medicines in the past. The food purpose must be seen as prevalent in this case, especially when the producer does not intend the product to be used as a medicine and where this is clearly evident from the packaging.

Thus, in view of the above, the desired distinction between foods and medicines must be shifted in favor of foods, i.e., we have to admit that also foods may have at least a preventive function, as in fact they do have and as has been affirmed historically.

It is true that a food supplement can be sold both as a dietetic food as well as in the form of a food of general consumption. The difference is mainly due to the definition of purpose.

Dietetic foods are foods that are directed towards a specific nutritional purpose, which has to be clearly put in evidence on the label.

Foods of general consumption, including food supplements, are not specific. They are offered without a special dietetic objective. However, we must, as already said above, be aware of the fact that even general consumption foods may have at least a preventive function against illnesses and disorders, as well as the capacity to cause changes in the build and the function of the body.

In connection with the definition of food supplements, the BGA's proposal mentions (under point 4.4) the term "nutritional need."

This term is considered equivalent with the daily recommended dose (RDA), without however saying one word about the difficulties that are connected with determining these daily doses. These difficulties arise from the fact that all individuals are different and from the lack of sufficiently accurate studies for many nutrients to allow a somewhat certain determination of the actual daily need.

This lack of reliable research is clearly evidenced in the report of the Scientific Committee for Food (EU): "Nutrient and energy intakes for the European Community, 31st Series (1992)," which is referred to by the BGA's draft.

The SCF committee in the report refers many times to insufficient data for single nutrients. The reports says about the RDAs for children that the recommendations are "best estimates" and that they should "perhaps be regarded as serviceable values for food labeling and planning purposes rather than definite statements of need."

The committee furthermore refers to the general lack of research in the EC and in the world at large and states that "the nutritional needs of the normal healthy individual are commonly classified as a low priority for medical research."

If now the BGA tries to make the availability of food supplements depend on such incomplete research, if one proposes to make "lists of allowed substances" and if the dosage of various substances is proposed to be limited to a largely unresearched "nutritional need," then this goes really too far. Obviously the objective here is not the protection of public health but the satisfaction of an exaggerated bureaucratic desire to control.

The Discussion about Positive and Negative Lists

Basically, the establishment of lists of nutrient substances, be they positive or negative, must be seen as an excessive bureaucratic effort to control. Food law is already sufficiently clear in not allowing toxic substances as part of foods. If there is a fear of undesirable side effects of some nutrient substances in higher dosages, then one should also think about the free availability of substances such as alcohol and tobacco, the harmfulness of which is hardly a point of discussion, or of simple sodium chloride, which is harmful in high dosages, without anyone thinking about limiting the availability of these substances.

Apart from the fact that it is impossible to produce a really exhaustive positive list, it is the very existence of such a list which would be a serious barrier to necessary further research. As pointed out very well by the SCF committee, medical research is not interested in researching nutrient substances. Furthermore, even food-oriented research would lack incentive for further research into a known substance if it was already included in a positive list, and on the other hand it would be discouraged from investing in research on a substance that is not included in the list.

Also, a negative list seems to make no sense, as can be seen reading the reasons given by the BGA in favor of making one. Reference is made to nutrients, for which there are insufficient data about normal or harmless levels of intake, to nutrients for which exist national or regional programs to increase intake in the population and to nutrients for which there is no need for supplementation in the population.

These arguments show even more clearly the general insecurity and the lack of data about single nutrients. It does not seem correct to take such a lack of data as a justification for the general prohibition of a nutrient substance. Furthermore, considerations about the nutritional status of population groups must not have an influence on the availability of food supplements used by individuals.

Even nutrients, for which "by reason of intoxications there is general agreement" and for the supplementation of which "there are no scientifically recognized reasons" do not, in our opinion, have to be completely prohibited. It would be sufficient to put an obligatory warning on the packaging or to limit such substances to a dosage that is recognized as having no side effects. This would satisfy both a desire to protect public health, as well as the freedom of citizens to determine their nutrition in accordance with their individual desires and their persuasions.

A positive or negative determination of the various forms of nutrient substances is not practicable because, even though the criteria for such a determination come necessarily from medical research, the use of these substances is not medical but nutritional. So we have to rely on medical research which, as already stated above, is available in sufficient quantity and quality only for few nutrients or forms of nutrient substances and if at all, it is available only because, at one point or another, a pharmaceutical company intended to market the nutrient or the specific form of nutrient substance as part of a medicinal product.

It is not correct however, to make the acceptance of a food or nutrient substance dependent on the more or less accidental availability of medical research. At least one would have to work out criteria for the safety of nutrients and of forms of nutrient substances that are acceptable to the food industry and the food-supplements industry, but such criteria would by necessity be different from the standards set for medicinal products.

Limitations of dosage

A limitation of quantity or dosage for single nutrients seems useful only where there is reasonable concern, i.e., where a serious danger to the consumer has to be avoided. This is the case for very few nutrient substances and is at present well taken care of by voluntary limitation of dosages by producers. In any case, there are exceedingly few cases of intoxication by nutrient substances even in the USA and in the Anglo-Saxon countries, even though for decades food supplements with dosages many times the RDA have been freely sold there. This cannot be said, however, of other substances that are freely available such as strong alcoholic beverages and tobacco. For these freely available substances, there are thousands of documented cases of intoxication, without anyone seriously thinking about limiting their dosages.

Even though protection of the consumer is an important objective, one should on the other hand avoid "protecting the consumer to death," i.e., we have to weigh the onerosity of the intended protection against the right of the individual to decide for himself, in order to avoid an excessive bureaucratic control of the citizen. These considerations must also include an analysis of the (possible) benefits of a free availability of adequate nutrient concentrations which allow the individual to arrange his/her own preventive measures by a sensible choice of nutrition. It must be left to the individual to decide what he regards as sensible. In any case, the "experts" of conventional medicine are not competent to decide, because their training does not include a knowledge of the latest research in this area.

We see that the usefulness of a limitation of dosages towards a maximum seems extremely doubtful. Also, a limitation towards the minimum is completely unjustified by considerations of consumer protection, unless the objective is to control the life of all citizens down to the smallest detail. It would be quite sufficient to demand complete labeling with clear indication of contents in units per dose or per tablet/capsule. All consumers would then be able to determine for themselves what exactly they are consuming.

Labeling

It seems useless to want to establish a special name for foods supplements. We are dealing with normal foods that consist mainly of one or more nutrients and other natural substances of high nutritional value. The nature of the product is quite clearly distinguishable from the packaging, without there being a necessity to create a new "product category."

As for dietetic food supplements, these are subject to existing regulations for dietetic foods.

We have nothing to add to the demand for complete labeling, although the usefulness of a listing of the recommended daily doses and of a percentage of these seems doubtful, especially in view of the uncertain and scarce research data and the orientation of daily dosages as population reference values, not as individual needs.

There is nothing to be said about point 6 (products for adults). However, it seems to be unnecessarily restrictive to a priori exclude health-related claims because foods and especially foods with a higher concentration of nutrients can very well have a preventive function and it seems unreasonable to not inform the consumer about this function.

The BGA's Draft Regulation

Considering what is said above, the project for a Codex regulation on food supplements would at best have to be seen as superfluous. In any case, however, it would be an unjustified limitation of the right of free development of the personality, which must include the right to freely choose one's own nutrition.

If, on the one hand, we cannot deny the necessity of consumer protection, on the other hand there is an important right that is just as worthy of protection, the right to free development of the personality and the right to self-determination. Furthermore, an analysis of damage vs. usefulness is necessary. The extremely small damage that unregulated food supplements can effectively cause and the usefulness (especially in view of the continually rising costs for the single states for medical care and for the treatment of chronic illness) of the free availability of these substances for public health, must be thoroughly analyzed before getting into a hasty over regulation of this product category.

Therefore, it seems basically doubtful whether a regulation for food supplements as proposed by the BGA is at all justified. However, in the case of a decision to proceed, it would be necessary to proceed with great caution, because the catastrophic situation of medicine today, especially with regard to prevention, has become an extremely critical factor for the single states and an over regulation of alternative ways to maintain health, including that of nutrition, could lead to a rapid and possibly irreversible worsening of public health.

We recommend, therefore, to drop the idea of a regulation of food supplements in the area of Codex Alimentarius and in the contrary case, to proceed with the greatest caution and only in agreement with the industry concerned.

AUTHOR'S NOTE: The German (original) version is dated 14 April 1994, and was sent, with a letter of the same date, to the General Secretary of the European Health Product Manufacturers Association (EHPM) in an effort to make the EHPM take on the Codex fight. The English version is dated 15 April 1994. There was no publication at the time, and EHPM chose not to take up the matter in any strong way. I sent the comments around by letter at first and by email and as far as I remember, only years later (some time in 1998 or 1999) I published the comments in both languages on the site of La Leva di Archimede.

Despite Victory Over one Codex Proposal the Need Remains for Further Activism

By John C. Hammell

(Published in *Life Extension Magazine*, September 1996)

While an international effort to regulate and restrict vitamins worldwide was beaten back setback this Summer, public and private moves on a number of fronts in several countries still pose a threat to health-care freedom.

A victory has been achieved in Geneva, Switzerland, at the executive committee meeting of the United Nation's Codex Alimentarius Commission. When the German representatives tried to advance their Codex proposal which threatens worldwide access to high-potency vitamins, the concern of other countries helped push back those efforts to an earlier phase in the testimonial process.

The German proposal still threatens to reduce consumer access to dietary supplements to no higher than recommended daily allowances. If successful, the proposal would become the international reference standard under the NAFTA and GATT international trade treaties. Numerous supplements would become unavailable.

And there are other concerns. Codex functions like a board of directors meeting in that the only official things that occur are what are noted in the minutes of the final report. Thus, the Canadian proposal to create a negative, or "no trade," list of herbs appeared to have been defeated during the meeting, but because no express statement was made in the final report to kill this proposal, an independent "expert" panel could be convened on this topic at any time without a vote of the Codex Commission.

International Advocates for Health Freedom contributed to the victory by sounding the alarm to allied groups around the world who rallied their citizens in opposition to the German Codex proposal. The war is just heating up, however, as Codex harmonization efforts continue at high speed in countries around the world.

Citizens worldwide need to continue to oppose Codex Canadians need to help sustain the two lawsuits filed against the Canadian Health Protection Branch, and fight for the "foods are not drugs" amendment. The British need to oppose an effort to limit consumer access to Vitamin B6 to just 10 mg. And Americans need to resist the effort to give new enforcement powers to the Food And Drug Administration, and resist as well over-the-counter drug status to herbs and botanicals. Form letters on the International Advocates for Health Freedom website and via fax on demand make it easy to keep fighting the forces threatening free access to dietary supplements.

A Proposal Knocked Back

Suzanne Harris of the Law Loft in Colorado attended the Codex executive committee meeting in Geneva at the end of June. Harris also was able to procure information vital to the struggle by gaining access to the World Trade Organization briefing on the Committee on Sanitary and Phytosanitary Measures.

The German proposal could have been accepted by the Codex Commission at step 5, bypassing the remaining three steps in the process, if no nation had objected to its acceptance. It could have progressed to step 6 if a "consensus" of the Commission had agreed. Under the Codex procedure, this is the point where nations can draw attention to economic problems for domestic industries that any proposed guidelines would cause. This also is the stage at which work proposals can be dropped altogether or pushed back to an earlier stage in the process.

Opposition to the German Codex proposal began with the Netherlands, which has special status as the head of the European Union. According to notes taken by Harris at the meeting, Dutch representatives stated, "We have some difficulty here. The area is a minefield. There was fierce opposition in the committee. Also, essential parts in square brackets remain unresolved. How can we advance this proposal to step 6 when there is so much uncertainty? We have reservations. We do not agree to advance this proposal to step 6.

Canada agreed with the Netherlands, requesting that, "Development of the proposal should cease altogether. In our view, consideration of this proposal could interfere with the development of international practices. A significant number of consumers believe that they have a right to consume these vitamins and minerals. Worldwide guidelines are not required. Canada strongly opposes adoption at step 5. We recommend that (1) we cease development of these guidelines altogether, or (2) at least return the proposal to step 4."

German representatives then admitted there had been controversy, but argued forcefully that only seven out of 39 countries had argued against adoption of their proposal at step 5, and stated that the Commission had to decide if the proposal should advance to step 6, or return to step 3.

United States representatives then declared, "This is not an appropriate topic for international standardization at this time . . . ."

Australia, New Zealand, and Japan then strongly endorsed the position of the U.S., Canada, and the Netherlands. South Africa agreed with the Netherlands not to advance to step 6, but argued that work shouldn't be discontinued, while Norway, Austria, and Hungary supported Germany, calling for a continuation of the work.

The chairman of the committee then stated, "I see a consensus to return the proposal to step 3. We need a fundamental re-thinking on the developing discord on this issue." Thus, while the long-range German Codex proposal suffered a major setback, ongoing harmonization efforts continue full throttle in individual countries. There will be further reports on both the long-range and ongoing harmonization threats via an E-mail distribution list. Send E-mail to International Advocates for Health Freedom at jham@concentric.net to be added to the list. Donations to Suzanne Harris to continue her work can be sent to The Law Loft, P.O. Box 709, Johnstown, Colo. 80534, USA.

Canadian Update

In Canada, International Advocates for Health Freedom has

been able to catalyze widespread awareness of the Codex threat, and has assisted Freedom of Choice in Health Care in filing two lawsuits against the Health Protection Branch in order to stop the third phase of "cost recovery," which threatens to drive small Canadian supplement manufacturers out of business. If successful, these lawsuits will stop the Health Protection Branch from violating people's rights under the Canadian Charter of Rights and Freedoms, will challenge an overly broad definition of what constitutes a "drug," and will block imposition of an illegal tax that was never debated by Parliament.

Donations and assistance are badly needed to keep monitoring the HPB and to sustain the legal effort. Send donations to Freedom of Choice in Health Care, 5863 Willow St., Suite 711, Willowdale, Ontario M2-1J8, Canada. For more information call 416-690-5558. To assist the British Columbia chapter, call 604-793-9087.

United Kingdom Update

New legislation has been introduced in the United Kingdom to limit free access to Vitamin B6 supplements above 10 mg in strength. Under this proposed law, supplements of Vitamin B6 of greater than 10 mg would become licensable medicines. Products containing up to 200 mg of Vitamin B6 have been on the market in the U.K. and U.S. for decades without adverse reactions reported at that dosage level (there have been reports of neurologic symptoms in some people consuming 500 mg a day or more of vitamin B6 without the other B complex vitamins).

The toxic dose of Vitamin B6 in dogs is 3,000 mg per day. The British government's advisors, known as the Committee on Toxicity, say this should be divided by a factor of 300 to arrive at the safe dosage level for humans of 10 mg, but leading science policy experts consider the factor of 300 to be arbitrary, not based on scientific evidence.

This is a good example of the threat of Codex harmonization. Consumers should be alarmed at this threat because the United Kingdom is the world's second largest manufacturer of dietary supplements. If the U.K. arbitrarily regulates Vitamin B6 at 10 mg, ignoring volumes of safety data presented by the Council for Responsible Nutrition and other organizations, what would stop them from limiting consumer access to other nutrients to RDA levels? If the U.K. harmonizes with the German Codex proposal in this way, we could lose them as an ally and the Germans could still push their proposal through.

Consumers worldwide must come to the aid of people in the U.K. Letters protesting this restriction on Vitamin B6 should be faxed or mailed to two key members of Parliament: Jeff Rooker, M.P., House of Commons, London SW1A 0AA, U.K., fax +44 171 219 5823; and Paul Boateng, M.P., House of Commons, London SW1 0AA, U.K., fax +44 171 219 4970.

United States Update

Over-the-counter drug categorization for herbs and botanicals in the United States is being pushed by the National Nutritional Foods Association, the Utah Natural Products Alliance, and the American Herbal Products Association, apparently under the influence of German phytopharmaceutical companies with designs on the North American market.

It appears that the National Nutritional Foods Association and Citizens for Health (which also supports this move) don't even want their own members to know that they are pushing for herbs and botanicals to be regulated as OTC drugs. At a discussion on Codex they sponsored at the recent National Nutritional Foods Association convention in Las Vegas, there was no mention of their advocacy for herbs and botanicals being regulated as OTC drugs.

The recent report by the Dietary Supplements Label Commission recommends that herbs and botanicals be treated as OTC drugs, and has other provisions to restrict freedom in health-care. Although the Commission Report doesn't carry the force of law, Congress is strongly influenced by reports of this kind, and could try to repeal the gains made by consumers under the Dietary Supplement Health and Education Act of 1994.

It is important to understand that some of the larger dietary supplement companies may not mind this because they can afford the added bureaucracy, but it could drive smaller competitors out of business. Competition helps keep prices down; it doesn't help consumers when smaller companies are squeezed out of the market, especially when those on top are the major pharmaceutical companies.

The Dietary Supplements Label Commission's report was

released very quietly, and the vast majority of dietary-supplement consumers in the U.S. are unaware of it. It also provided a much-too-short period of time for public comments. The 77-page draft report can be obtained by calling 301-650-0382.

By press time, the comments period will be over. However, since FDA may still use the report to attack the supplements industry through rule-making, it is important that Americans fax or mail letters protesting the report's recommendation to make herbs and botanicals OTC drugs. They should protest the fact that adequate time has not been given for commentary on the report.

Fax or send your letters to Kenneth D. Fisher, Ph.D., Executive Director, Commission on Dietary Supplement Labels, Office of Disease Prevention and Health Promotion, R.728G Hubert H. Humphrey Building, 200 Independence Ave., S.W., Washington, D.C. 20201, phone 202-401-6245, fax 202-205-0463. Your senators and Congressional representatives can be called through the U.S. Capitol Switchboard at 202-225-3121 for the House, and for the Senate 202-224-3121. If you don't know their names, just state your state and zip code and they will connect you.

Further information about these issues and form letters to help you register your protests are available by telephone at 800-333-2553.

The Codex Alimentarius Commission

By Tamara Thérèsa Mosegaard
MayDay, Denmark

(The original version of this was published in the *MayDay Newsletter*
in 1999, and later updated on the MayDay website.)

The Codex Alimentarius Commission has been jointly established by the Food and Agriculture Organization of the United Nations (FAO) and the World Health Organization (WHO) as an instrument for international cooperation in the field of Food and Agriculture.

After applying for observer status several times MayDay was invited by the Danish Ministry of Food and Agriculture in the Spring of 2000 to participate as an observer on its national delegation at the Codex Committee on Nutrition and Foods for Special Dietary Uses (CCNFSDU) meetings in Germany.

This national-delegation observer status has given us access to more closely follow the work of and within the Codex Alimentarius, as it has also given us the opportunity to meet new international health-freedom colleagues, with whom we exchange information and insights into the complex world of international (restrictive) global legislation.

MayDay is skeptical about this "invention" of the WHO and FAO meetings where they have begun discussing food recommendations, which are the inspiration for several unnecessary and highly-restrictive European Union (EU) directives concerning nutrients.

We are critical of the fact that:

- The Codex Alimentarius Commission consists of a gathering of non-elected government bureaucrats from many countries in the World;
- Real consumer organizations are very poorly represented at these meetings;
- Codex is creating food recommendations that usually turn out to be restrictive regulations on health promoting substances such as dietary supplements;
- Under the pretense of promoting free trade, the Codex Alimentarius Commission is really blocking it - especially free trade in dietary supplements (and herbs);
- Codex is highly centralized and driven from the top down by an elite;
- Codex works to create global standards called "harmonization," which do not at all honor the diversity of needs and interests of the World's many different peoples and biological types;
- The Codex meetings are not generally open to the public;
- International and national media have not been showing any interest in such an important forum;
- The Codex meetings are not discussed publicly in the media, which is why far too few people have actually heard of the existence and work of the Codex Alimentarius Commission.

[Since June 2000, MayDay has participated as an observer at the annual Codex Committee meetings in Berlin and Bonn, Germany - working closely together with its colleagues from the National Health Federation.]

Codex Alimentarius Information - an Introduction.

By Alex Dybring
and Tamara Thérèsa Mosegaard,

(Published in the MayDay Newsletter, September 1999)

The World Trade Organization (WTO) was founded in January 1995. It succeeded the less-effective, free-trade organization General Agreement on Tariffs and Trade (GATT) with the following essential innovation when disagreements arose: the majority votes of the WTO were then binding. In GATT the losing or disagreeing party had a possibility of blocking the final decision.

About 128 countries – among others, Denmark – are members of the WTO, whose stated purpose is to liberalize World trade, exploit the World's resources better, increase living standards, ensure employment, work for a sustainable - development, and maintain and protect the environment.

This may all sound very sensible, though some people find it a somewhat contradictory, if not impossible, task that the organization wants to both exploit the World's resources optimally while it is working for sustainable development and for protecting the environment.

The real problem is that the WTO seeks to obtain these goals by, for example, decreasing tariff rates and harmonizing and thereby equalizing the many different habits and legislations in the many various countries.

The philosophy of the WTO is that equalization and harmonization will benefit free trade and economic growth and thereby stimulate development, also in the social area, and it is this noble idea coming from the WTO that many like so much.

In the area of food – and foods for special dietary uses – the World Health Organization (WHO) and the Food and Agriculture Organization (FAO) under the United Nations (UN) in 1962 created the organization called the Codex Alimentarius. The task of this organization made up of non-elected government bureaucrats is to prepare global standards and harmonize guidelines for global food legislation.

If you like the thought of a World Government, this actually comes pretty close. At least it does when it is about what you would like to eat and drink – but only to someone who may think this is an institution that is concerned with "consumer protection."

Part II

(2000-2005)

Codex to Meet Again: Health Freedom at Risk

By Scott C. Tips

(Published in *Whole Foods Magazine*, June 2000)

Guess what the following events have in common. On January 1 of this year, Ireland converted major herbal products into prescription-only drugs. And in just three months, some 40% of South Africa's health food stores have closed down. If you guessed El Niño, you're wrong. If you guessed the Codex Alimentarius Commission, then you're correct.

As you should know by now, the Codex Alimentarius Commission (an organization of the Food and Agriculture Organization of the United Nations and the World Health Organization) is charged with, among other things, creating international "guidelines" for vitamin and mineral supplements. These guidelines would eventually be adopted by all signatory members of the General Agreement on Tariffs and Trade (GATT) in order to harmonize and replace national dietary-food regulations. The proof that they would be more than just "suggestive" once adopted is evident in the actions of Ireland and South Africa, both of which acted under the influence of Codex.

Make It or Break It

The French (who invented the word bureaucracy) and the Germans (who then elevated that word to its highest art form) are intent on pressing forward with limits on both potencies and the range of vitamins and minerals that can be sold. At the last meeting of the Codex Committee on Nutrition and Foods for Special Dietary Uses ("CCNFSDU") in September 1998, they pushed to advance the guideline review along the path to completion. Fortunately, the Americans, British, and Japanese, among others, kept the German proposal for restrictive guidelines from advancing. Instead, three delegations (Canada, the European Commission, and the United States) were charged with drafting a neutral discussion paper on the subject for presentation at the next CCNFSDU meeting. That meeting is set for June 19-23, 2000, in Berlin, Germany; and it could be the make-it-or-break-it session for determining whether restrictive guidelines advance or not.

The discussion paper that the five delegations drafted (Brazil and Mexico joined the original three) is only a summary of the range of issues and perspectives that have arisen in committee discussions on the subject of vitamin and mineral supplement regulation. The United States' actual position on the issue is being developed as this article is being written and will be evident by the time you read these words. You can find a copy of the discussion paper on the web at an FDA website specifically set up for interested viewers (http://www.fda.gov/foi/foia2.htm).

As a summary, the discussion paper and the proposed draft guidelines make it clear that most of the Europeans would like vitamin-and-mineral supplements to be tightly regulated and not to be sold in a free and open market. Right out of the chute, the draft guidelines are heavily biased to the restrictive European viewpoint: if a country's laws treat vitamin-and-mineral supplements as drugs, then the Codex guidelines would not apply to those supplements since the Codex guidelines are intended only for food. Therefore, the precious European national laws making drugs out of natural vitamins and minerals would not be touched. The only touchable laws would be those food and dietary supplement laws that treat vitamins and minerals with actual concern for consumer freedom of choice. The playing field has thus been ipso facto unfairly defined.

Next, the proposed guidelines would permit supplements to only contain those vitamins, provitamins, and minerals prepared "in conjunction with the relevant Codex standards whose indispensability for human beings has been proven by scientific data." Leaving aside for the moment the debate as to the minimum and maximum levels of those vitamins and minerals to be permitted, this proposed section contains a fool's definition. For most of us who have already dealt with the FDA's and orthodox medicine's definitions of "substantial scientific consensus," we could have a frontal lobotomy and still understand that the regulators will define numerous nutrients to not be "indispensable" according to proven "scientific data." Orthodox scientific data is virtually always lagging well behind the knowledge curve; it will be no different with Codex guidelines. Say goodbye to anything other than those vitamins and minerals recognized as necessary for daily dietary intake.

Say No to Mandated Levels

Minimum levels mandated for vitamin and mineral supplements are yet another intended bureaucratic restriction. While ostensibly not as onerous as mandated maximum levels, minimum levels still suffer from the "fool's paradise" mentality that arrogantly thinks that present-day humanity knows all that will ever be known (or should be known) about recognizable vitamin-and-mineral levels of consumption. Moreover, in saying that supplements must contain at least 15% of the recommended daily intake (RDI) of a particular vitamin or mineral or it cannot be marketed and sold, the Codex regulators forget that sometimes there might be a space problem in a capsule or tablet. The manufacturer might have to omit that extra vitamin or mineral because it was only, say, 10% of the RDI. For some countries' populations, that lost 10% RDI could be important. And in any country, that lost 10% RDI would be a nutritional loss regardless. In my view, it is better to have some nutrient intake than none at all.

The proposed maximum levels are one of the real nightmares here. The German-led Europeans would dearly love to limit vitamin and mineral supplement potencies to 100% of RDI. And while I have frequently been a critic of FDA's policies and practices, we must give FDA credit for having listened to the health industry and having strongly resisted at Codex committee meetings the imposition of any maximum levels of potencies. That the Japanese, British, New Zealanders, Dutch, and others have supported the United States in this regard reflects credit upon those countries as well.

'Positive' & 'Negative' Lists

Another nightmare, though, is the German-led European proposal to create "positive" lists of vitamins and minerals that would be allowed in supplements. Any nutrient not so listed could not be sold. Again, we face the arrogance of thinking that present-day bureaucrats and scientists have discovered all of the nutrients that could possibly exist. It is a good thing for us that such a list was not mandated by a Codex-type organization in the 1920s; more than half of the vitamins we know today would not even be on the list.

A proposed alternative to the "positive" list is the "negative" list that would simply prohibit the sale of any nutrient listed on it. If such a list were adopted, all non-listed vitamin and mineral supplements would be generally permitted for sale. Although not as onerous as the "positive" list, the "negative" list still suffers from the virtual certainty that the regulators will list nutrients that they have decided, in their infinite wisdom, retailers cannot sell and consumers cannot use. "Deadly" tryptophan is one such candidate that readily comes to mind. Other amino acids and melatonin are additional, probable targets.

As with most problems, there are opportunities also created by the problems. The opportunity here is that, with organized effort, the Codex process could even be turned to our advantage if it results in the adoption of pro-health-freedom Codex standards that would permit European and other citizens the freedom to buy and consume something more helpful than the pipsqueak vitamins and supplements they now have. Only time, and your efforts, will tell.

MayDay as Observer of Codex Alimentarius

By Tamara Thérèsa Mosegaard,
Healthwriter

(July 2000)

In the field of food and applied nutrition, the World Health Organization (WHO) and Food and Agriculture Organization (FAO) launched the Codex Alimentarius Commission in 1962. The task of the Commission is to establish global standards, guidelines, and recommendations for food; and now their biannual meetings have been increased to annual meetings due to the many issues on its agenda.

After many petitions to the Ministry of Food, MayDay was granted permission to observe the Codex Alimentarius Commission (CAC). At CAC's 22nd convention on the topic of nutrition and diet foods, Rachel Santini from the Danish Institute for Common Health (DIFF) participated on behalf of MayDay, and I participated in the beginning of June 2000.

The meeting took place at the German Directory of Foods in Germany and covered four days. 230 people were present, with an equal representation of both sexes. The majority of the delegates were non-elected governmental representatives, more than a fourth represented industrial interests, and only about ten were delegates from Non-Governmental Organizations (NGOs), thus representing consumer groups independent of governments. At least one government delegate from each country had the right to speak, together with a few industrial representatives, while nearly no consumers held the same privilege.

he agenda contained 14 items, such as Labeling regulations, gluten-free products, breast-milk substitutes, children's foods, enriched ("functional") foods, as well as the notorious vitamins and minerals guidelines, which threaten slowly to stifle access to applied nutrition on a global basis.

It deserves mention that around 1500 protesters gathered before the meeting for a whole day in Berlin to demonstrate for free access to food supplements. The first day of the CAC meeting saw a gathering of 1,000 protesters – predominantly former patients who had benefited from applied nutrition – and speeches were made by Dr. Matthias Rath, leader of the demonstration, Norwegian writer and supporter of food supplements Dag Viljen Poleszynski, and the New Zealand heil practitioner Gene Sylvester Eagle-Oden, who spoke on behalf of 5,000 heil practitioners from New Zealand.

That same evening, a German newsflash accused Matthias Rath of "seducing his poor patients in his fight against Codex which he only fought because he himself made a living of selling applied nutrition and using them in his treatments." It was significant that the Codex Alimentarius meeting was not mentioned at all in the ten-minute-long news item, which was so detailed that it must have taken more than half a day of preparation, and, consequently, must have been made in advance.

In fact, CAC's fundamental and express aim is allegedly:
- to provide food safety, and
- to secure trade and avoid trade barriers.

After scrutinizing the list of participants and being present at the meeting, we must conclude that items one and two have changed place so that profit seems to go before health. To be sure, critics of the CAC maintain that trade makes up 95% of their interests whereas only 5% is left for health.

The heated debate about global guidelines for breast-milk substitutes divided the delegates into two groups consisting of representatives from the poor, developing countries versus those from the Western (mostly European) industrial countries, as these naturally have interests that differ widely as far as nutrition, politics, and economics are concerned.

The Western breast-milk substitute industry is interested in entering the vast market of the developing countries; whereas, for reasons pertaining to health and economics, developing countries such as India and quite a few African States strive to enable their populations to breastfeed their children for as long as possible.

Poor people seldom have access to pure water, they are often unable to read information labeling, and can rarely afford the expensive breast-milk substitutes. Milk powders that must be mixed with a proper measure of water – clean water, that is — are not as practical to a mother in a poor mountain village in Africa as they are to a mother in the West with access to cleaner water and with a financial status and schooling that make her better equipped to mix the breast-milk substitution.

Research showing beyond a doubt that breastfeeding is the healthiest choice for children under the age of six months was totally disregarded in WHO's contribution at the meeting. On the whole, the discussion about breast-milk substitutes exemplified the difficulties concerning the setting of standards, guidelines, and recommendations valid on a global basis and to peoples with widely different conditions, needs, and interests, and setting these standards means addressing a huge clash of interests.

Moreover, CAC repeatedly points out that the CAC standards are only *recommendations*, which the individual governments may choose to follow. It is quite common, however, that governments adhere to the CAC guidelines, for which reason the guidelines agreed upon in this forum are of paramount importance.

Consequently, it is also noticeable that larger biotech and pharmaceutical industries are richly represented whereas representatives of actual consumer interests are few and far between and have very little say in the matter.

When, during the debate on functional foods, we hear the very same arguments brought forth in favor of these that were shortly before produced in evidence against vitamins and minerals when such were the issue, it is only natural to suspect that hidden agendas were at large.

To be sure, critics of the CAC do feel that the organization has aimed for some time at two underhanded issues:

1. That transnational medical industries agree on trade regions in order to monopolize the applied nutrition

market – an arrangement that does not create healthy products but rather the opposite.

2. That these global industries introduce functional foods and genetically modified organisms in food and applied nutrition at the expense of the quality of applied nutrition.

The latter is particularly problematic in the eyes of health-conscious, supplement consumers since both governments and consumer organizations become marionettes in a large-scale game about the "safety" of consumers and monopolies that are difficult to see through for the individual consumer.

Through MayDay's GMO campaign, I work for the right to choose for myself what I consume. I wish to be able to avoid genetically modified organisms (GMO) in my food and applied nutrition, while at the same time I campaign to retain access to dietary supplements in the high doses necessary to maintain my life quality and health.

However, dietary supplements in high doses predominantly comes from the USA, where a majority of food production is based on genetic engineering, so if I wish to retain my fundamental right to choose, I must also look out for GMO in certain types of supplements (no GE on the labels).

Unfortunately, at the meeting it was agreed to regulate vitamins and minerals according to so-called "maximum levels," which to consumers used to optimal and therapeutic doses in fact look more like "minimum levels."

There was talk about a positive list of vitamins and minerals and about introducing a rule that manufacturers in the future must inform about the percentage of "recommended daily allowances" (ADT/RDA) on their labels, which, according to MayDay, will only delude consumers into believing that they receive more nutritional value than is actually the case. This is what is normally referred to as "consumer misguidance" if conducted by private companies, but in this case the perpetrators are the official governments.

The excuse is "consumer safety" because we – the poor, stupid, ignorant consumers – cannot be allowed to take too much (read optimal doses) of the so-called "dangerous" vitamins and minerals

– for what would happen if we became too healthy?

It was at this point at the meeting that we could easily have been led to believe that the issue was the protection of citizens against the thousands of deadly chemicals running rampant on the market today, but it turned out that the real issue was actually the micro and macronutrition products vital to the growth, balance, energy, and very existence of our bodies.

According to the many Codex bureaucrats, it must now be made more difficult to obtain access to the beneficial and completely harmless nutrition products such as the vitamins and minerals that many people consume in order to maintain their health, and we must ask ourselves who benefits from this, other than the large pharmaceutical companies that will become future distributors to the population.

The meeting contained a reference to a recently published survey conducted by the National Academy of Sciences, USA / Canada, which concluded that "there is insufficient research to support the theory that larger doses of antioxidants such as selenium, Vitamin C and E, carotene, and beta-carotene can prevent chronic diseases."

Since no Danish delegates to the CAC have read this survey as yet, we must wait to deal with it in depth until a later MayDay newsletter, in which we hope also to be able to elaborate further upon the issues concerning the globally damaging influence of Codex Alimentarius on nutrition and public health.

Nothing is what it seems to be when it comes to Codex Alimentarius, and its increase of power will undoubtedly lead to a world-wide decrease of self-determination in regard to what and how much people wish to consume, which is a very bad sign, if you like freedom to choose and it does not make any sense if you remember that the Codex was supposed to ensure free trade and avoid trade barriers.

Important issues like the freedom to choose your own food and nutrients and your health are now in the hands of a few hundred food bureaucrats who frequently and quite unrestrainedly convene in Germany, the stronghold of large-scale medical industry, because they are convinced they know what is "best" for us.

If vitamins cause illness, then mine are defective.

- Scott Tips
(paraphrasing Ted Nugent)

Breathe Easier -
Codex Adjourns

By Scott C. Tips

(Published in *Whole Foods Magazine* – September 2000)

Berlin in June 2000 was hot and humid, the hottest it had been there since 1947. Still, despite the weather and the demonstrators outside the German Federal Institute for Health Protection of Consumers and Veterinary Medicine building, it was cool inside as the various delegates assembled on the morning of the first day of the Twenty-Second Session of the Codex Committee on Nutrition and Foods for Special Dietary Uses. As a member of the U.S. delegation to Codex, and thanks to the National Health Federation which paid my expenses, I was one of those many persons arriving that Monday morning to take part in the on-going process of establishing international food standards. It proved to be an interesting week.

Upon entering one of the ugliest buildings I have ever seen, the delegates were confronted with many tables piled with numerous Codex documents translated into several different languages. The noise level was remarkably low despite the many people moving amongst the tables, collecting documents, and then drifting on to the free food-and-drink table dispensing, among other things, over-sized German pretzels. Looking back out through the huge windows to the street, you could see the demonstrators starting to hoist a huge anti-Codex banner into the air with the help of a mobile crane.

The United States delegation, numbering some fifteen persons, had its own pre-Codex meeting inside the building in one of the smaller rooms. Chaired by Dr. Elizabeth Yetley of the U.S. Food and Drug Administration, the meeting lasted almost an hour as members of the group became acquainted or re-acquainted with one another and the woman chosen by the Food and Drug Administration to head and speak for the delegation at the Codex meeting itself. Dr. Yetley gave each of us a chance to voice our views and concerns on certain Codex topics. Many did not speak up, I did. If you have read this column before, then you can easily guess my expressed opinions on such Codex agenda items as prohibited vitamin-and-mineral lists ("negative lists"), "approved" vitamin-and-mineral lists ("positive lists"), and mandated minimum and maximum potencies for vitamins and minerals, all of which I oppose. I quickly became known as the "radical" of the group, although I did not learn this until later.

The actual Codex Alimentarius meeting itself took place in a grand auditorium that had narrow, fold-down chairs arranged in semicircular rows that inclined steeply downwards until the lowest row ended just before the small floor where the chairman's and secretariat's table was placed. It had the appearance of being a long way down even though it wasn't. There was a small, long and very narrow table fixed before each row of chairs so that there was some space for writing. The head of the person seated in front of you came about even with your own table. I was seated almost directly behind Dr. Yetley, which later turned out to be fortuitous.

The chairman was a German, Dr. Rolf Grossklaus, who ran the Codex meetings in an innovative (to me at least) way. After much discussion on a topic, and especially after the German government delegate did not seem to have anything more to say, the chairman would somehow psychically determine that a "consensus" had been reached or not reached by the delegates and the group would move on to the next topic of discussion. I never once saw a vote taken or even the slightest hint of a show of hands; the outcome was all calculated in Dr. Grossklaus' marvelous brain as he scanned the room and remembered how many had spoken for or against each proposal. Of course, the squeaky wheels counted the most; the silent ones not at all. We Americans, who suffer from this obsessive notion that votes must actually be counted before deciding upon an outcome, might learn much from this economical and quick means of "voting." In fact, stupid me, why even vote when the chairman could just decide for all of us?

However, despite this time-saving "consensus" means of voting, the agenda advanced slowly. If the head delegate of a country or NGO (non-governmental organization recognized by Codex) wanted to speak, then he or she would raise that country or group's white sign with its name on it and wait to be recognized by the chairman. Certain delegates, such as the woman delegate from India, really liked to drone on and on, especially when an opportunity presented itself to lambaste any suggestion that dietary supplements be freely sold. The Norwegian delegate, who shared this view, would often glare at us Americans when Dr. Yetley expressed her views. In contrast to these two women, Dr. Yetley was, I thought, polite, professional, measured, and very diplomatic in her expression of the U.S. Government's official views.

Those views, though, were not always consistent with my own or those of my clients. On the Codex dietary-supplement topics of maximum and minimum levels of vitamins and minerals as well as positive and negative lists, the official U.S. position was to push for limits and lists based upon "science-based risk assessment" methods. The thinking here is that while there will be, for example, limits on vitamin potencies, they would be higher than the current laughable levels in most countries. Some countries, such as France, caught on to this, arguing against such standards because this "toxicological-studies approach would result in the levels being fixed too high"! The French then elaborated that the potency level should not result in an intake of more than 15% RDI for each pill. Unfortunately, this general opinion was not uncommon among the Codex delegates, many of whom thought that vitamin and mineral supplements containing 100% of the RDI would be ample.

But the French were not the most vocal opponents of freedom of choice at this Codex meeting. By far, the Norwegians and Indians took that prize. The official American view that "science-based risk assessment" methods of determining potency limits should prevail presumes that these other countries will be forced into accepting higher potency limits based on scientific studies rather than their current, vague national policies. This view also presumes that we Americans will not be forced to accept such limits due to our own national dietary laws (especially, the Dietary Supplement Health and Education Act of 1994 and the 1997 FDA

Modernization Act). Why the Codex standards would apply to others and not to us was never adequately explained to my satisfaction. Given the current rate at which the United States is being internationalized, my own opinion is that Codex standards would make mincemeat out of any domestic American legislation.

The other potential problem lies in the siren call of "science-based risk assessment" methods. Like brandishing a crucifix before a vampire, one need only utter the words "science based" to make most opponents recoil in fear. That is because science is supposed to be fact based and therefore objective. But science, like anything else, can be manipulated to exclude unorthodox, but still valid, viewpoints. One need only consider the sad fate of those academics who have dared challenge the HIV-virus-as-the-cause-for-AIDS hypothesis to understand that far from being bastions of free thought and the exchange of ideas, most universities and scientific bodies are engines of conformity. Grant money and academic tenure will almost always go to the conformists, not the mavericks.

The risk, then, in adopting such science-based risk assessment standards is that they will not be fair and objective, but will instead be used to create artificial barriers that restrict freedom of choice. And compliance with those standards could be equally difficult if lengthy, expensive, drug-like tests, trials, and clinical studies must first be conducted before the standards are established and implemented. On the other hand, there is merit to the claim that the Europeans would be better off with vitamin-and-mineral potencies based upon this standard rather than their current, completely bureaucratic standard.

In the end, after four days of discussion, the Codex agenda on vitamin-and-mineral guidelines had not advanced appreciably. The Codex way of leaving a topic open for future discussion is to "bracket" that text upon which no consensus has been reached so that it may be considered at the next Codex meeting. There were many brackets inserted around the text at this Session, only a few removed, and no real progress towards finalizing the Codex Guidelines on vitamins and minerals was made.

Interestingly enough, on the final day, when the wording of the draft Report of the 22nd Session of the Codex Committee was being discussed and debated, Dr. Yetley unilaterally asked the chairman to delete from the Report the U.S. position stressing the importance of consumer choice and access to vitamin and mineral supplements. No one else on the U.S. delegation seemed to take note of this, but from my position seated behind her, I was able to quickly pass her a note strongly objecting to the deletion. After discussions with her at the break, and with the later support of another member of the delegation, Beth Clay of the Congressional Committee on Government Reform, Dr. Yetley was convinced to reinstate the deleted language, which she accomplished with finesse.

The Session adjourned that Friday afternoon, June 23rd, and the delegates went their separate ways, not to meet again for another year or so. Although Dr. Yetley and the other FDA personnel running the American delegation were truly attentive to the views of its members and permitted their expression during our private meetings, it was equally apparent that they had their own plan to push. Only the U.S. delegate, Dr. Yetley, or her alternate, was permitted to speak out at the Session for our delegation. The only exceptions were those few members who were also NGO members recognized by the Codex Committee and separately seated at the Session. Those NGO members could directly speak out on issues of concern to them, which was an advantage for them.

Someone once wise-cracked that "no man's wallet is safe so long as the House of Representatives is in session." These are words that could easily apply by analogy to one's vitamin cabinet while Codex is meeting. So, breathe easier - Codex has adjourned and is no longer in session - at least for another year.

These are my principles.
If you don't like them, I have others.

- Groucho Marx

International Law Trumps Domestic Law

By Scott C. Tips

(Published in *Whole Foods Magazine*, January 2001)

It is a tragic commentary on the American media that the extraordinary event of which you are about to read has to come to your attention first, not through a local or major national newspaper or through the television news, but instead courtesy of a monthly industry magazine. We are so inundated with "news" wherever we turn that we can easily delude ourselves into thinking that we are well-informed about all newsworthy events. Unfortunately, as I hope you have noticed, the news is so selected and so filtered by the time it is slickly offered to you – like so much processed, plastic-wrapped cheese – that it rarely resembles reality. When you have the chance to compare, for instance, European reporting upon American news events with American reporting on American news events, you notice a difference that is at times remarkable. Truly important news goes unreported more often than you would suspect.

The extraordinary event alluded to above is that, for the first time in American history, the United States Congress voted to change a domestic law because we were told to do so by an international body. Considered "unthinkable" only a few months before, and despite clear constitutional prohibitions against its actions, Congress knuckled under to the World Trade Organization's (WTO's) dictate that the United States must change its tax laws governing foreign sales corporations. In particular, the WTO objected to the fact that U.S. tax law exempted from the income tax a small portion of income earned abroad by U.S. corporations. WTO called this a "subsidy," even though most European countries do not tax their own corporations on any income they earn abroad. The

WTO handed the U.S. an ultimatum to change this law by October 1, 2000, or else.

How We Joined the WTO

For those of you not familiar with the World Trade Organization, it is an international bureaucratic body established to "manage" international trade. In December 1994, in its twilight hours and in the wake of the sweeping Republican congressional victories that would soon hand control of Congress over to the Republicans, a lame-duck United States Congress voted to have the United States join the WTO. Both the Republican and Democratic party leaders cooperated to quickly push this legislation through with little discussion before "fresh faces" could take office and possibly derail the process.

Nearly six years later, we are truly historical witnesses to the inevitable logic of that WTO membership. During its final days, the 106th Congress has voted to change American tax laws to comply with WTO's bureaucratic dictates. The significance of this action to you, the reader, is far more important than that a single section of the U.S. Tax Code was changed. Even those who are confused by the ballots in Florida's Palm Beach County can figure this one out. We are looking at the legislative equivalent of the visible panty line, or the camel's nose in the tent.

For all too long, you and I have heard from all quarters how the Codex Alimentarius Commission, or Codex, will not have any impact upon U.S. domestic laws governing dietary supplements, especially the Dietary Supplement and Education Act of 1994 (DSHEA). Even members of our own industry have reassured us how Codex will not impact domestic laws such as DSHEA. Others have disagreed. Now, we have the evidence.

If the WTO can dictate domestic changes in our tax laws, then you can be absolutely certain that all of our legislation is vulnerable to international dictates. The precedent has been established and will continue to be reinforced in the future. Eventually, we will all forget how laws used to be made and come to think that non-democratic WTO and other international-body dictates are normal. Not only environmental, labor, and tax laws, but food, dietary-supplement and other domestic American laws, will be increasingly subject to international review and revision. Unfortunately, few outside the United States are as receptive to consumer freedom of choice as are we, so you can be certain that our single vote in these international bodies will not count for much.

Welcome to the future. It's just a shame that you can only read about it here.

A government that is big enough to give you all you want is big enough to take it all away.

- U.S. Senator Barry Goldwater

Comments on My Trip to Codex

By Susan Negus, Ph.D.

(Berlin, Germany, November 26-30, 2001, the Codex Committee
on Nutrition and Foods for Special Dietary Uses (23rd Session))

In November of this year, I had the privilege of being selected to serve on the United States Delegation for Codex in Berlin Germany. I had heard about the Codex Alimentarius Commission and its efforts through its Committee on Nutrition and Foods for Special Dietary Uses to control what supplements and levels of those supplements could be sold, but I never really gave it much thought. I did not think that this could possibly happen in the U.S. where we have had the freedom for so long to use natural vitamins and supplements far more freely than elsewhere. As I sat there, with headsets on so I could hear one of the four language translations, I soon realized how wrong I was. I was listening to a group that was setting guidelines that would restrict what and how much of a vitamin (among other things) I could buy.

Codex is a group of 75 countries and organizations from all over the world that meets periodically for the purpose of developing an international food code to ensure quality and safety based on sound scientific fact. The group's stated and seemingly ethical goal is to insure consumers that they are getting safe, wholesome food, as well as being protected from unfair trade practices. In theory, there appear to be great benefits for having standardized products that are structured to be safe for consumers; but, in reality, it doesn't work because of the hidden agendas, nearsightedness and greed of the leaders involved. Also, controls and restrictions really only limit the options and choices of an individual. In reality, these "guidelines" will only act to restrict what can be included in these products and take away consumers' freedom of choice and ability to make their own decisions. If anything, this bureaucratic, "top-down" mentality that the government knows best what you and I should be permitted to consume is nothing more than incredible arrogance that history has proved wrong over and over again. As they say, the road to hell is paved with good intentions.

Codex participation dictates that a country's delegation must be led by a government employee. This results in some interesting dynamics. Governments tend to be about regulations and control, not about individual freedoms and choices. The head of our U.S. delegation is Elizabeth Yetley, PhD., a lead scientist for the Nutrition Center for Food Safety & Applied Nutrition for the Food and Drug Administration (FDA). Dr. Yetley appeared to have very specific opinions regarding what she would support, and it appeared to be consistent with the FDA agenda. As spokesperson and the only member allowed to speak to the assembly, when members of the U.S. delegation voiced differing points of view to her, she would not share those views with the full assembly even when they were consistent with U.S. law.

The representation of the subjects of debate can be questioned. Delegates from other countries and groups shared privately that the heads of their delegations would often not voice the opinions of their groups. In addition, when reasonable points were presented to the full assembly that did not support the control position (for example, the issue of the individual's ability to assimilate vitamins), certain other participants would at most acknowledge the point made but then simply dismiss it and the agenda would move on.

The scope of the Codex guidelines of what constitutes a food product is expansive and includes not only food labeling, additives, contaminants, etc, but also nutritional products (vitamins and minerals) which they consider to be foods. By including these "nutritional products" in their scope, they are drawing guidelines that will standardize vitamins and minerals (among other things; such as, baby formulas, diet and energy products - and, ultimately, everything) worldwide - so that trade between the various member countries will supposedly be assisted by standardized product composition and labeling. Unfortunately, it also means that freer countries (such as the U.S.) are being drawn down to the far more restrictive standards of the less-free countries (such as Norway and India).

Another example of matters addressed is infant formulas. Among the guidelines, in the development of baby foods, is one dealing with informing mothers how they will feed their babies. The delegation from India wanted pictures on labels so illiterate people (who are in the minority in their country) would know how to use these products, yet they ignored the fact that most of these same people cannot even afford to buy the baby formula. Instead of educating mothers, the mentality of "treating the symptom but not the disease prevails." This mirrors the problem with the health-care system; instead of helping the body repair itself, the symptom is suppressed. By limiting our freedom to choose how we treat our bodies, we only succeed in keeping people ignorant and at the mercy of government control (and mistakes).

One major implication that the U.S. government delegate is completely ignoring or won't talk about has the most potential for devastating impact. The U.S. has trade agreements with most of the countries participating in Codex. If these Codex "guidelines" are put into place, the U.S. will be forced to change U.S. law to match the guidelines if the U.S. wants to continue doing international trade with these countries and avoid trade sanctions. Of course, the U.S. manufacturers would be forced to follow these new U.S. laws.

Some argue that this could not happen in the United States. However, it has already happened. In October 2000, the 106th U.S. Congress changed the U.S. Tax Code to comply with a World Trade Organization's (WTO) bureaucratic dictate. (Reference; International Law Trumps Domestic Law, Whole Foods Magazine, January 2001, page 72). Because the U.S. had voted to join the WTO in 1994, it was now bound to the WTO's bureaucratic dictates and forced to change its law to comply with those dictates.

Many delegates within the U.S. delegation at Codex saw the possibility that pharmaceutical companies could successfully lobby the U.S. Congress to allow high dose vitamins only by written prescriptions from medical doctors if the U.S. was forced to restrict the maximum amount of vitamins in a product. These products would most likely be manufactured by pharmaceutical companies in the U.S. - not the natural products' industry.

If you believe that control of vitamins could not happen, be careful. It's happening right now as the European Union (EU) is currently working on legislation to standardize vitamins and minerals. As recently as December 6th in London, The Times ran an article discussing how in January 2002 the EU will pass, for the second time, a directive in the European Parliament that will establish maximum levels for vitamins and minerals. Their next step is to establish what those maximums are.

In the past, Codex, regarding only the area of vitamin and mineral supplements, has agreed to the following:

(1) The scope would include "vitamin and mineral supplements intended for use in supplementing the daily diet with vitamins and/or minerals. These Guidelines apply to vitamin and mineral supplements which are regulated as foods." The following, taken directly from the Codex Agenda Notes states, "It is left to national authorities to decide whether vitamin and mineral supplements are drugs or foods. These Guidelines do not apply where products are regulated as drugs." In other words, these guidelines would not apply if vitamins and minerals were sold as drugs (controlled by the pharmaceutical companies) and required a written prescription from your doctor. This means the game is rigged from the outset; those countries that already regulate their vitamins and minerals as drugs do not have to comply with these Codex guidelines, while those countries that allow freer consumer access to vitamins and minerals will have to abide by these drug-like restrictions. "Heads, I win; tails, you lose." That's not my idea of a fair bet.

(2) Again taken from the Codex Agenda Notes, composition of the vitamins and minerals "may contain all vitamins and minerals that comply with the criteria" which "shall contain vitamins/provitamins and minerals in conjunction with the relevant Codex standards whose nutritional value for human beings has been proven by scientific data" which is "a single nutrient or an appropriate combination of nutrients." This means that vitamins and minerals must have scientific studies that show what they can be used for and whether they can be used alone or in the appropriate combination (which must also be proven scientifically). Unfortunately, in reality, the results of most "scientific" studies are a consequence of

large payoffs to the companies testing the products. Even worse, the economic costs of engaging in drug-like clinical trials to satisfy the drug-oriented mindset will enormously increase the product costs of natural products that have been in use for decades or longer and that are far safer than drug-company created synthetic alternatives.

(3) Labeling must include the statement that "supplements should be taken on an advice of a nutritionist, a dietician or a medical doctor." This is a troubling insult to consumers because it implies that they are not capable of making intelligent choices about what to take to improve their health. Unfortunately, the limited knowledge medical doctors have on vitamins and minerals does not even remotely qualify them to advise people on them.

Despite opposition from some members of the U.S. delegation committee, Dr. Yetley (the U.S. FDA government representative) did not protest the following issues which gained consensus:

Minimum & Maximum Contents of Vitamins and Minerals were discussed. It was agreed that it would be necessary to set minimum and maximum dosages for particular ingredients in an approved vitamin or mineral product. Reasons stated for controlling high-dose vitamins were: (1) safety and (2) so people would not use them as meal replacements - particularly in Third World countries. While Codex continually stressed that everything must be scientifically based, no research was presented to show how high-dosage vitamins were unsafe. It's interesting to note that no adult has ever died from an overdose of vitamin or mineral supplements. Unfortunately, the FDA cannot make that claim regarding prescription drugs they have approved.

The actual minimum and maximum amounts are still under discussion, but the current status of the debate is leaning toward imposing a minimum of between 15% and 33% (equal to one meal) of Recommended Daily Intake (RDI) in each serving. Also not agreed to, but currently being discussed, is a maximum amount of 100% of the RDI.

If imposed, this would mean consumers could not get high-dose vitamins (except possibly with a prescription from a medical doctor).

Also, this would eliminate the choice to use very small amounts of a vitamin in a product where this would have a synergistic effect. Another concern is that under these restrictions, it is very possible that vitamins without established RDI amounts would no longer be available.

In listening to the various discussions it became apparent that the "guidelines" being created were not intended to be just suggestions. They were to become equivalent to laws stating exactly what will be allowed and not allowed.

Is this situation inevitable or can we protect our rights? I see the following as possibilities for you to consider:
- Get informed
- Tell others
- Find Internet sites with credible information
- Respond when provided opportunities to register your opinions
- Encourage people attending Codex meetings to stimulate debates.
- Support organizations that oppose Codex "guidelines.

Hundreds of thousands die each year from pharmaceutical drugs and yet Codex is concerned about our intake of vitamins and minerals. As Harry Masterton-Smith, the chairman of Consumers for Health Choice commented, "I'm allowed to smoke myself to death and drink myself under the table, so why can't I take perfectly safe vitamin and mineral supplements?" The only explanation is that it is politically motivated and not motivated by so-called "concerns" for the health and welfare of the public.

The horror of the reality of Codex sends chills through my body. I probably wouldn't believe how serious it is except for the fact that I sat right there and watched it happen. I cannot encourage everyone enough to do whatever they can to let people know about this and take any action - no matter how small it may seem - to stop or at least slow down this group which is restricting our ability to make choices regarding our health. Like I used to think, you may think it will never happen; but let me tell you, it is happening now!

The next Codex meeting is scheduled for November 2-6, 2002 in Berlin, Germany. Past Codex progress can be reviewed in their web site at: http://www.codexalimentarius.net.

Codex Gets one Step Closer to Control

By Scott C. Tips

(Published in *Health Freedom News* & *Whole Foods Magazine* 2002)

For us Southerners, Berlin in November 2001 was dark and cold. The bitterly cold wind off the Spree River blew through the city and sent leaves and pedestrians alike scattering across the pavement for cover. And at this time of year, and at this high a latitude, the sun sets early. By 4 p.m., the sun has disappeared over the horizon and the big department stores are lit up like traffic accidents. But the coldest and darkest place of all was in the meeting hall of the German Federal Institute for Health Protection of Consumers and Veterinary Medicine building where the Codex Alimentarius Commission was holding its week-long session.

As I arrived on the drab, gray morning of the first day of the Twenty-Third Session of the Codex Committee on Nutrition and Foods for Special Dietary Uses, I was confronted by virtually the same anti-Codex demonstrators as had been outside the building during last year's meeting. With festive blue-and-white party balloons adorning the nearby tree and the demonstrators' huge banner blowing in the wind like a sail, anti-Codex media crews shoved cameras in my face seeking any words of wisdom that I might have about Codex. One member of the group filled my arms with a huge spiral-bound anti-Codex petition. I decided to get even with him, so I gave him a copy of my previous *Whole Foods* article on last year's Codex meeting. He smiled bravely, poor thing, clutching my article as I left him to walk past the guards and enter the building.

The Issue At Stake.

Thanks once again to the National Health Federation, which paid my expenses, I was there as a second-time member of the U.S delegation to Codex. The issues are important: International vitamin and-mineral regulations are being slowly but surely established that will determine not only what vitamins and minerals you can take but in what amounts and at what levels as well. A rapidly shrinking number of our own industry members are still pretending that U.S domestic legislation will protect us from these harsh international standards; but, as I (and others) have pointed out before, the danger is a gradually encroaching one if not an immediate one that will eventually overwhelm American protections against such madness If you boil frogs, you gradually turn up the heat so that they do not sense the danger and try to escape. In this case, we are the frogs and the heat is being gradually increased every year.

The Codex Meeting.

Once inside the building, I scooped up the Codex meeting documents that had been placed on the tables near the entrance, grabbed a quick bite to eat from the free-food counter, and moved on into the meeting hall where the other delegation members were taking their seats. There were a few new faces, but it was a meeting much like the previous one in June 2000.

The important discussions picked up where they had last left off and focused on the international "guidelines" that were to be established for vitamin-and-mineral dietary supplements. The Codex chairman, a German named Dr. Rolf Grossklaus, kept insisting that these standards under discussion were only "guidelines" and "not standards," implying if not actually stating that no one need therefore be overly concerned. Guidelines are of course voluntary, but because of World Trade Organization (WTO) membership obligations prohibiting its members from engaging in unfair trade practices, member countries may be sued and heavily fined if their trade practices do not conform to adopted international standards. We have already witnessed at least one instance where the United States Congress was forced to rescind domestic American law governing international business corporations because of a WTO dictate. So, far from being "guidelines" as we might think of them, once adopted, these guidelines will have a very real bite and they will restrict vitamin and mineral potencies at ridiculously low levels.

The irony is that these rules will only have a bite on those countries where citizens already have the relative freedom to buy and consume those vitamins and minerals they want and at effective levels. Countries that have already classified vitamins and minerals as drugs, such as Germany, are exempt from these Codex rules. They do not have to change a single law, rule, or regulation. Only those countries that classify their vitamins and minerals as foods will be affected. It is a rigged game, from the outset. And it stinks.

Minimum Levels

As I sat there in my fold-down seat in the meeting hall and read the Codex guidelines and heard the various government delegates speak, I was struck by the incredible ignorance on parade. Many of the countries such as Canada and Australia had sensibly enough written in their discussion papers that there should be no lower limits on vitamins and minerals unless claims of potency were being made, but when it came time to speak up against lower limits, no one really did. Dr. Elizabeth Yetley, the U.S. delegate, was especially passive and weakly asked for clarification, even though I had just given her arguments against lower limits in our pre-meeting before the general session.

The discussions very quickly degenerated into simply a question of establishing the minimum levels for vitamins and minerals, not considering whether they should be set at all. Not a single one of the government delegates had the moral fiber to argue strongly against the imposition of a minimum level, even those who had opposed them in writing. So, the Codex rule is being established that no vitamin or mineral supplement may contain less than 15% of the Reference Daily Intake (RDI). Countries such as India want the minimum level to be 33%, while others such as Norway and Cuba want the minimum to be 25%.

Besides the obvious moral problem of prohibiting people from freely and voluntarily contracting with one another as they wish, the practical problem with minimum levels is that they foreclose manufacturers from adding something useful (such as a vitamin or mineral) in a capsule or tablet instead of something worthless, like a filler or excipient. In my view, it would be better for a person to get some additional nutritive value from a capsule or tablet, than nothing at all. I pointed this out to Dr. Yetley, while another U.S. delegate (representing the American Holistic Association) thoughtfully added the argument that special formulations exist that would in the future be prohibited because they could no longer include sub-minimum levels of vitamins and minerals. To my mind, the higher those levels are set (e.g., at 33% as India wants), then the more the consumer will be hurt. If countries are concerned about wild health claims being made for low potency vitamin supplements, then there are other ways to address that concern. As the Canadian delegate argued on paper (but not in the discussions unfortunately), you can simply restrict wild claims from being made. In fact, establishing minimum levels comes from the same mindset that would prohibit everyone from driving on public roads in order to stop accidents and save lives. The intention might be laudable, but the implementation of that goal is irrational, if not outright stupid.

Maximum Levels

In setting maximum levels for vitamins and minerals, the Codex meeting saw the real "fight." But, again, it was never a fight between those forces arguing against implementing maximum levels and those forces arguing in favor of such limits. Once more, it was the typical control-oriented, bureaucratic mindset that saw the two sides only arguing over how the maximum levels would be set. Like Hitler and Stalin battling it out with each other, the issue of freedom of choice never was even considered; it is simply a question of which dictatorial rules you will be forced to live under.

The debate, then, was between the RDI (or RDA)-based group and the "nutrient appropriate risk assessment" group. The RDA-group (primarily Third World countries) wants upper (and lower) permissible levels set at a percent of the RDA, while the second group (such as the U.S.) wants the upper limit to be based upon "science-based risk assessment considerations, as determined by appropriate risk analysis methodology."

The Council for Responsible Nutrition (CRN) was in attendance as a non-governmental organization and argued both in a written position paper and at the meeting itself against the RDA-group's position. As CRN correctly pointed out, if safety is the ssue, then the RDA is the wrong standard to apply because the RDA was never defined to address safety and none of the data that were used to establish RDAs is even pertinent to safety issues. CRN's position paper zeroed in on the defects in the RDA-group's position when it said, "RDA-based limits are arbitrary and not related to safety, and thus carry the potential to be harmfully restrictive. With the progress in nutrition research, any assumption that the RDA represents safety is, in effect, imposing limits based on current knowledge of the benefits related to higher intakes nutrients [sic]. Calcium, folic acid, and vitamins C and E are examples of nutrients with higher needs recently recognized by increased RDA from the U.S. National Academy of Sciences."

Nevertheless, despite its insightful skewering of the RDA approach, CRN is a grand cheerleader for the second, alternative approach that would set upper-potency limits based upon scientific analysis. While this approach based upon "science-based, risk assessment" methods is more rational and is certainly preferable to the simplistic RDA-based approach, it is still fatally flawed because (once again leaving the moral and ethical considerations to one side) any upper limits would be set in stone, or at least hard-to-change clay, that could never keep up with the rapidly accumulating knowledge on nutrition. By their very nature, government rules and regulations can never change quickly enough to keep up with advances in human knowledge. In the meantime, countless thousands of people will suffer, even die, because they cannot have access to those health products that the latest advances could bring them.

The other fatal flaw in the "science-based, risk assessment" method is that it is probable that the upper limits would be based upon faulty data. I have heard that the director of one of the major scientific institutions processing these types of data has admitted that her facility did not have enough funds to collect and process the data correctly. So, the old expression, "garbage in, garbage out" still applies. As we should all know by now, just because something is dressed up in fancy and impressive scientific clothes does not make it so. Scientific data, like anything else, can be manipulated, ignored, suppressed, or even out-and-out wrong.

Moreover, the "science-based, risk assessment" method addresses the wrong question. With almost all vitamins and most minerals there is no toxicity issue at even the high doses many Americans consume. In court, I would have no problem defending vitamins and minerals by comparing their death toll to that caused by prescription and OTC drugs. As even CRN admitted, "Many vitamins and some minerals are so nontoxic that setting safety limits would be an idle gesture." So, why with the impressive safety record of dietary supplements must we spend so much time, money, and effort establishing "safety" limits? I guess these countries just have money to burn, or certain other industries want to restrict the competition.

In this sense, the "science-based, risk assessment" method, once implemented, could greatly increase the cost of your vitamins and minerals because they would essentially have to be safety-tested. I myself have made it through those 30-plus years of my life that I have taken vitamins without having been poisoned by them and I am willing to take that chance for another 30 or more years. Under this scheme, however, I would be protected from myself by the Codex dictates; but at a cost that would come at a steep price. If new drug approval expenses are any indication, the costs for this unnecessary increase in safety would be enormous. And only large companies could afford to compete.

Approved Vitamins/Minerals Only

One of the more insidious Codex provisions states: "Vitamin and mineral supplements shall contain vitamins/provitamins and minerals in conjunction with the relevant Codex standards whose nutritional value for human beings has been proven by scientific data." All of my previous points concerning the flaws of upper and lower potency limits for vitamins and minerals apply equally to this attempt to restrict the sale of vitamins and minerals to only those approved by Codex. There is no need to repeat those points here. Just bear in mind the disgusting fact that there was no opposition to this provision. Even though such a provision clearly violates American dietary-supplement law, the U.S. delegate sat through this provision's discussion and approval as if she were listening to last year's farming statistics. I have seen more excitement out of comatose patients.

Final Analysis

At last year's meeting, there was at least an argument that Codex might be salvageable in some way. Unfortunately, this year's meeting was the definitive nail in the coffin. Upper and lower limits have been approved, it is just a question as to where to set those limits. The "approved" vitamins-and-minerals concept is solidly in place. It is all downhill from here because no one ever takes a firm position in favor of freedom of choice. Everyone, including Dr. Yetley, is content to not rock the boat and let matters take their natural course. Despite my flurry of protest notes and suggestions to Dr. Yetley throughout the course of the Codex meeting, unlike last year, nothing positive resulted from my efforts.

I think that Dr. Yetley and the FDA truly believe that it is worth sacrificing freedom of choice so long as the "science-based, risk assessment" method is implemented. But as Robert De Niro quipped to Dustin Hoffman in the movie "Wag The Dog" after he had convinced the CIA agents to free and not kill him, "they are nice enough people, they just hadn't thought it through." They do not see that they are giving up everything in exchange for nothing, a chimera that will disappear and leave us all with nothing but chains.

So what to do? For those various countries that are already predisposed to freedom of choice, strong delegates must be put in place who will dig in their heels and reverse the erosion. Your voices must be directed to your representatives and the government, as well as the FDA, expressing your disgust with the FDA delegate's approach and telling them, in no uncertain terms, that if the United States (or your other country's) position in Codex does not change immediately, then the United States (or other country) should withdraw from the process and those ties that bind us to the process. "Harmonization" is no more worth the heavy price that will be exacted in this decade than appeasement was worth the cost in the 1930s. The sooner we realize that, the better off we will be.

*The jawbone of an ass
is just as dangerous a weapon today as in Samson's time.*

- Richard Nixon

AHHA Attends
Berlin Codex Session
What Did We Learn?
By Suzan Walter

*Report from Suzan Walter,
president of American Holistic Health Association,
on her attendance at November 4-8, 2002 session of
Codex Committee on Nutrition and Foods
for Special Dietary Uses (CCNFSDU)
in Berlin, Germany.*

Some things have to be experienced to be believed. A Codex Committee session is one of these. This report is to share my experience with you.

The Codex document *Guidelines for Vitamin and Mineral Supplements* and the potential for negative impact on access to nutritional supplements in the U.S. sparked my interest in Codex matters. After researching this in order to develop the website www.codexinfo.org, I felt a strong sense that I needed to be at the CCNFSDU session in-person to share some of my concerns. I was able to arrange permission to attend with media observer status.

The 223 people attending this CCNFSDU session represented countries from every continent plus international special interest organizations. The Committee agenda had 10 items related to international trade standards. This report will focus on Agenda Item #6 - development of the document *Guidelines for Vitamin and Mineral Supplements*.

General Impressions

The polarization on issues is dramatic. Picture a situation where groups with opposing positions each insist that their way is the only way. Issues involve the very different needs of developed and developing countries. Delegations come from both democratic and dictator-led governments. Regarding use of vitamin and mineral supplements - some groups are convinced that a normal diet is sufficient, and nutritional supplements are rarely necessary. Others stress the value of supplements and remind us of existing science validating how dietary supplements can enhance health and reduce the risk of disease. Regarding the issue of how much is "too much" - one side passionately insists any more than an established daily requirement of a nutrient is dangerous. The opposing side asserts that maximum safe limits must be established by scientific risk-assessment research.

The Chairman controls what happens. Professor Rolf Grossklaus, the German Chairman of CCNFSDU, determines who can speak, how long discussions on an agenda item will last, and the consensus of the assembly. Delegations may submit written Comments prior to the session. However, during the session, they are ignored and a delegation must have permission from the Chair to present their written "Comments" verbally. In order to be recognized each delegation has a mic with a request button they hit when they want to speak. This lights up on a board in front of the Chair. The Chair directs which mics are opened for comments. No votes are taken. The Chair normally listens to what is said by various delegations, then states what he views the consensus of the whole assembly to be. If people speak up that they disagree with that, the "decision" may or may not be changed. A summary report of what took place at the session is presented on the last day. Delegations can request corrections, but the Chair has the final say as to what is put into the report as approved changes.

Progress is painfully slow. With the combination of the divergent positions on issues and the way that the session deliberates, it is not surprising that hours can be spent on the wording of one sentence. There is no mediator working to negotiate a middle position or something that can gain general consensus. Note - the *Guidelines* document has been developing since 1988.

Press exposure is discouraged. My admittance to the Codex session was with a badge marked Press. When I asked where the press section of the auditorium was located, I was informed that there was none. The press had not been invited to cover this event. Others with Press badges were, like myself, interested individuals who were not part of any delegation. One individual with a press badge told me he had arranged for a video crew, but the crew was denied permission to enter the building where the meeting was held. Another day a man seated near the back of the auditorium was observed using a camcorder. The Chair announced that the filming must stop or the meeting would be adjourned. Obviously, they do not wish media exposure.

Actions on Guidelines

With the background of these general impressions I now relate what I observed during the CCNFSDU session in regards to Agenda Item #6 - *Guidelines for Vitamin and Mineral Supplements*. (If you aren't into details, jump to the Summary at the end of this section.)

Discussion on all of the agenda items was scheduled for Monday (9am-6pm), Tuesday (9am-6pm) and Wednesday (9am-8:30pm). The Chair allowed one agenda item to take up most of two days. At 7:15pm on Wednesday evening, the Chair finally started discussion on Agenda Item #6.

The lead delegate from South Africa read a statement reminding the assembly of the scientific research supporting the value of vitamin and mineral supplements, including research quoted from a recent *Journal of the American Medical Association* article that recommends that adults take a multi-vitamin daily. There was actually applause from the assembly after her statement.

The lead delegate from the United States suggested that all decisions should be based on data grounded in science. She also recommended that all Guidelines statements be changed from "shall" to "should," as this document is to be *suggested* Guidelines. The lead delegate from the European Union suggested that the title of the document be changed to add the word "Food," making it *"Guidelines for Vitamin and Mineral Food Supplements."*

The lead delegate from South Africa proposed replacing the current Guidelines Preamble with a totally new version.

Current Preamble:

"Most people who have access to a balanced diet

can usually obtain all the nutrients they require from their normal diet. Because foods contain many substances that promote health, people should therefore be encouraged to select a balanced diet from food before considering any vitamin and mineral supplement. In cases where the intake from the diet is insufficient or where consumers consider their diet requires supplementation, vitamin and mineral supplements serve to supplement the daily diet."

Suggested revised Preamble:
"People should be encouraged to select a balanced diet. However, vitamin and mineral supplements are useful in cases where dietary intake of vitamins and minerals is inadequate to either correct nutrient deficiencies or to supply prevention such as to reduce the risk of disease."

Somehow the discussion became one about how supplements as defined by the Guidelines are not to be used to treat disease. Comments were cut off on a procedural technicality that South Africa had not included this in their published Comments. The Chair did agree to include the suggested new Preamble in the final Committee report.

Note that all of these discussions involved suggestions or statements of support (or lack of support) for the matter being addressed. No mention was made of actual changes being finalized.

The next matter addressed was *Guidelines* section 1.0 Scope. There were a number of suggested changes for section 1.1:
Current:
"1.1 These guidelines apply to vitamin and mineral supplements intended for use in supplementing the daily diet [if and where necessary] with vitamins and/or minerals. These Guidelines apply to vitamin and mineral supplements which are regulated as foods."

Numerous delegations supported deletion of the phrase [if and where necessary] in the first sentence. The two sentences in 1.1 were addressed individually, with suggestions involving deletion or moving to another section.

One delegate suggested that the scope of the *Guidelines* be expanded to apply to food supplements with other ingredients.

Finally, attention was focused on what most of us considered the most important issue to be addressed - Maximum Levels - 3.2.2 (option #1) and 2.3.3 (option #2):

Current:

> "*3.2.2 [The maximum level of each vitamin and/or mineral contained in a vitamin and mineral and mineral supplement per daily portion of consumption as suggested by the manufacturer should not exceed [100%] of the recommended daily intake as determined by FAO/WHO.]*
>
> *3.2.3 [Maximum amounts of vitamins and minerals in vitamin and mineral supplements per daily portion of consumption as recommended by the manufacturer shall be set, taking the following criteria into account. (a) upper safe levels of vitamins and mineral established by scientific risk assessment based on generally accepted scientific data, taking into consideration, as appropriate, the varying degrees of sensitivity of different consumer groups; (b) the daily intake of vitamins and minerals from other dietary sources.*
>
> *Setting the maximum levels, the reference intake values of vitamins and minerals for the population should also be taken into account.]*"

Comments from delegations fell into three groups. Understand that this was NOT a vote. Of the 83 delegations, only a very small number were recognized by the Chair and had an opportunity to state which option they supported. The following is offered to give you a general idea of positions and is not a complete list:

Supporting **Option #1** - 3.2.2 - Maximum levels not to exceed RDI. Norway, Brazil, Indonesia, Thailand, Malaysia, and Nigeria.

Supporting **Option #2a** - 3.2.3 - Maximum levels based on risk assessment-European Union (representing 15 countries), Japan, Korea, and the United Kingdom.

Supporting **Option #2b** - 3.2.3 - Maximum levels based on risk assessment, but deleting the final sentence.
 United States, Switzerland, Canada, and Peru.

The lead delegate for the National Health Federation commented that research on the safety of vitamins has already been established. NHF did register support of Option #2b, but only as a very last resort.

By now the 8:30pm closing hour was fast approaching, and there were still two other important agenda items to be addressed. Discussion on Agenda Item #6 was closed, but first the Chair seemed to me to lecture the Option #1 RDI group. He stated very strongly that this is about safety (so consumers are not harmed), not needs. In addition, he commented that upper safe limits are not dosages.

On Friday, we assembled to review the draft report that outlined what transpired at this session. This report is not structured as detailed minutes, and does not list which countries were for or against a position. From 8-9:30am Friday morning the delegates scrutinized the report looking for errors and/or omissions. When we assembled at 9:30am, one by one the Chair allowed comments on each item in the report. When Agenda Item #6 was reached, I was very surprised to see that the Chair had incorporated three suggestions into the Guidelines as official changes. During the Wednesday evening discussions I had never heard him state that consensus had been reached. This would have allowed opposing delegations to speak out. Apparently I was not the only one surprised. Numerous delegates disagreed with the Chair's decisions. One delegate stated that her delegation's request light was on, but not honored. The Chair responded that she should have registered a complaint at that time. (How was she to know to complain?)

Summary
 When the dust settled, the following were the official changes.

"Title - Guidelines for Vitamin and Mineral Food Supplements
Section 1.1 These guidelines apply to vitamin and mineral sup-
plements intended for use in supplementing the daily diet [if and where
necessary] with vitamins and/or minerals. These Guidelines apply to
vitamin and mineral supplements which are regulated as foods.

These changes do not appear to be significant. So, this year no
real progress has been made toward revising the *Guidelines* into a
document that all can support. Long-time participants are encouraged that several countries have switched to supporting Option #2
- Risk Assessment. Another indication that Option #2 will be the
ultimate choice is that the governing body of Codex has officially
adopted a preference for risk assessment.

CLICK HERE [http://ahha.org/Berlin_Report_2002.pdf] to
review the official report from this 24th Session of the Codex
Committee on Nutrition and Foods for Special Dietary Uses that
will be submitted to the Codex Alimentarius Commission for
review June 30-July 5, 2003. Agenda Item #6 is on pages 11-12
(paragraphs 87-100). The current draft of the *Guidelines for Vitamin
and Mineral Food Supplements* is in Appendix IV on pages 56-57.

Personal Activities at Codex

As I was not part of a government delegation nor an NGO
(non-governmental organization) delegation, I was free to focus on
networking with whomever I wished.

I initially focused on surveying delegates as to their understanding of how, once the Guidelines are finalized, this document would
be enforced. Everyone I spoke with erroneously believed that individual countries would be free to use the *Guidelines* as suggestions
and adapt them as they wished. Further, none were aware that the
World Trade Organization (WTO) has the actual enforcement
power, and the WTO does not view a "guideline" document as
optional. I found this extremely disturbing, as this indicated to me
that the people responsible for creating the document did not
understand how it would be used.

The next new awareness for me was related to an apparent conflict of interest. I was already aware that some countries designate
nutritional supplements as drugs and others as food, and that the
Guidelines are drafted to only apply when supplements are regulated

as food. This means that a number of countries who regulate supplements as drugs are drafting the Guidelines but will never have to abide by them. During my conversations at the Berlin session, I discovered that a number of countries use both designations. At lower levels of "dosage" supplements are treated as food, while at higher levels they are handled as drugs. Now I realize that the number of exempt countries is even larger than I thought. My reactions to this ... Why are the countries who are exempt fighting so hard to have the rules set up "their way"? How many countries on the CCNFSDU are exempt? Will the exemption be honored by the WTO?

By day two of the session I had become aware that no one was integrating the Comments submitted by a number of the delegations prior to the start of the session. I selected the first three sections of the *Guidelines* (Preamble, Scope, and Definition) and drafted a summary of input that incorporated those ideas that worked well together. I added a bit under the Scope section that would protect the document from WTO misuse. This sheet was shared with a number of delegations, resulting in some positive impact. However, the Codex procedural requirement that new ideas must be submitted in writing before the Committee session starts really hampers this type of mediating integration. No wonder it takes years to negotiate progress.

The opportunities I had to discuss various Codex issues at length with a number of the attendees were an exceptional privilege. There are a number of people who have been following *Guidelines* developments for a number of years. Some are still optimistic, while others throw up their hands and voice expectations that this will be going on for another five years or more. I look forward to staying in touch with these individuals from all over the world.

Now What?

Now that the politics of how Codex committees operate is better understood, the AHHA Board of Directors can strategize where we should put our efforts to enhance *Guidelines* activities between now and the November 2003 CCNFSDU session in Germany.

We might consider compiling data on WTO enforcement procedures and document how WTO expects to apply them to Codex standards and guidelines. Codex headquarters had informed us that enforcement will not be known until there have been a number of trade disputes processed by WTO - providing precedents for future decisions. This seems too important an issue to be left so undefined. Isn't it vital that those drafting the Guidelines are fully informed of how they will be used?

We might also consider reviewing past delegation Comments that have been overlooked. In Berlin I learned that many, many excellent ideas have been proposed, but ignored. Perhaps AHHA can resurrect some of these ideas for consideration in 2003.

AHHA is not a lobbying group. We will not be contacting delegations around the globe and trying to influence them to our way of thinking. AHHA is a 501(3)(c) educational nonprofit organization. It would be appropriate for us to research and document facts and share through our website at codexinfo.org, particularly areas where delegates are not currently fully informed. If you have ideas or feedback, send us an e-mail codex@ahha.org.

Liberty means responsibility.
That is why most men dread it.
- George Bernard Shaw

Who Decides About our Health?

Baby Foods, Nutritional Supplements, and "Codex Alimentarius"

By Sepp Hasslberger
(Rome, 9 November 2002)

Codex Alimentarius is the name of a global food-standard setting body that is attached to the Food and Agriculture Organization of the United Nations' WHO. The deliberations in Berlin this past week of a committee charged with developing guidelines for vitamin-and-mineral supplements have shown progress towards a risk-based approach for regulating vitamins and minerals. This is a positive development in view of the substantial agreement that had persisted in the past, for an RDA-based approach which would be disastrous for both consumers and industry, but especially for public health world wide.

Two days before the beginning of the week-long discussions which took place in Berlin from 4 to 8 November 2002, the Dr. Rath Foundation had organized a large conference attended by over 2500 people, where the results of scientific studies were made available. The studies and the personal successes of people taking vitamin supplements on the advice of Dr. Rath prove the overwhelming importance of changing from a pharmaceutical and symptom-based approach to illness to a nutrition-based, cellular-level approach. Perhaps more importantly, Rath's conference brought together a group of representatives of organizations from several countries, all concerned with preserving freedom of choice for natural methods of prevention and cure.

Two days later, on the morning that saw the beginning of the official Codex conclave, many of the participants in the Rath event were demonstrating outside the gates of the building hosting the meeting, loudly demanding that their health choices be respected.

Meanwhile, delegates from about 50 of the Codex member countries started to deliberate standards for baby foods. Agreement on this issue was as elusive as it has been for years, maybe more so now than ever. The greater issue of globalization can be observed, neatly compressed into the Codex "microcosm" for everyone to see. Multinational pharmaceutical and food industries, with the backing of a number of industrialized countries, try to pave the way for the global free sale of their products. This is greatly resisted by most of the developing countries and by consumer advocates who believe that babies are best fed on mother's milk. Developing nations believe that they should not be forced by an international standard-setting body to accept baby foods which are too expensive for most of their starving population and which, from a nutritional point of view, are admittedly inferior to "the real stuff."

These nations are worried that their traditional, natural foods and especially the practice of mothers breast feeding their children will be swept aside by the promotional abilities of the multinationals. An understandable worry, in the light of the "civilizing" progress that colonization has forced on the Third World for the better part of the past couple of centuries. Their economies are in shambles despite, and some say because of, "structural adjustment" measures forced on them by the IMF and the World Bank. Their agriculture unable to develop because local production cannot compete against agricultural subsidies given to their own farmers by economic empires such as the US and Europe. It seems that after a long sleep, the developing countries are waking up and are resisting. They perceive the imposition of standards made for global industries as an effort to re-establish colonial domination on the part of the industrialized nations.

Vitamin-and-Mineral Supplements

Days of deliberations brought little visible progress. Towards the end of the three-day conclave the subject of food supplements was once again on the agenda. Although the issue of supplements is in many ways quite different from that of baby foods, the same worries prevail with developing nations. They see vitamin-and-mineral supplements as another "blessing" to be bestowed on them by the same hated multinationals, the giant global pharmaceutical and food industries. We must view the Codex discussions on food supplements against this backdrop.

The proposal for a guideline on vitamin-and-mineral supplements, first made in 1994 by the German Codex delegation, seeks to extend the philosophy of control so prevalent in that nation and in much of the rest of continental Europe, to the whole World. The draft proposes to set strict limits on the composition and potency of these extra nutritional foods, relegating everything exceeding "nutritionally necessary" dosages to the world of medicine, a world which today is clearly dominated by pharmaceutical interests.

To be fair, some progress has been made over the years, at least on the issue of dosages, towards a consensus that would safeguard the rights of consumers to take care of their health in a manner consistent with their own choosing. More often than not, consumers see their nutritional needs in a way that differs remarkably from "official recommendations," and so do some medical doctors, witness the research of Dr. Rath, Linus Pauling, and many others.

Scientific Approach to Limits

Early in the discussions of this particular Codex session, the importance of a scientific approach to regulation was stressed by FAO, the Food and Agricultural Organization, and the WHO. The majority of delegates agreed that such an approach would be possible and indeed desirable. Risk analysis and risk management, an emerging branch of science, is part and parcel of such a scientific approach. Yet, on food supplements, the German chairman Rolf Grossklaus proposed to "protect consumers" for the next four or five years by establishing both lower and upper limits to product dosages, while waiting for the squadrons of risk managers to get up to speed.

Two options were to be discussed, RDA-based limits and risk-based scientific evaluation. Needless to say, no agreement could be reached which path to follow. While most of the industrialized nations including Europe and the US asked for a risk-based scientific approach, the feeling among some of the African, Asian, and South American developing nations was that this would open their markets to a host of products they could not control, a division of opinion reminiscent of the discussions on baby foods.

When discussing the preamble of the draft guideline, remarkably, the South African delegate strongly stood up for the free availability of supplements, to the extent of lambasting the participants for what she called a hypocritical approach to health and even a "return to the dark ages." In the face of scientific data indicating that supplementation is potentially life saving, Ms. Booyzen said, Codex should not be thinking of putting limits on safe products such as vitamin and mineral supplements. She suggested, quoting scientific studies, that supplements might be useful to prevent many of the diseases of civilization, the so called degenerative diseases which are due to sub-optimum supplies of certain nutrients in the body.

This was a refreshing new development, warmly welcomed by non-governmental delegations and observers concerned with consumer choice. In the more than lively discussion that followed, several delegations echoed the European Union representative who stated in full earnest that anything with preventive, let alone curative, properties must be considered a medicine and is therefore outside the Codex mandate and is not part of the things to be legitimately discussed by the Committee.

An Obvious Contradiction

The discussion brought a glaring, basic contradiction inherent in our health policy into plain view: We are told to eat fruit and vegetables, possibly five helpings a day, to stay healthy and to prevent heart disease and even cancer, yet we may not take the nutrients we seek in the form of supplements for the same purpose! It is another way of saying that "there is a pharmaceutical monopoly on medicine and health, that must not be touched." Food has nothing to do with health, according to this particular twisted view, and before you may even obtain high-power nutritional support, you must first get sick!

Respecting the existence and the overriding character of that pharmaceutical monopoly, the Codex Committee on Nutrition and Special Dietary Foods could not agree on the purpose of supplementation. Nutrients, after all, have nothing to do with prevention, which remains exclusive territory of pharmaceutical medicine. The preamble of the proposed guidelines therefore remained open to discussion. Chairman Grossklaus then proposed to concentrate on the issue of possible dosage limits so as to afford some temporary "protection" to consumers, but found that a divided assembly could not make up its mind.

What's the Score?

The "scorecard" of the discussions on dosage limits confirms our suspicions of a "larger game" going on in the background, unseen and unacknowledged by many of the participants. Far from living up to its fragile consensus on the necessity of introducing scientific risk management into decision making on public health, the committee's members again divided into two opposing camps.

The European Union and its member states voiced support for the "second option," that of letting science decide where the dividing line should be drawn between what is allowed and what is not. They were supported by Australia, New Zealand, the US, South Africa, Japan, Switzerland, Canada, the UK, and, remarkably, Russia, Korea and Peru. Norway was adamant, on the other hand, that its citizens should not have access to any supplement of vitamins and minerals that contains more than the RDA, the recommended dosage which is associated with an absence of the classical deficiency diseases such as scurvy, also called the "sailors' disease." No matter that scurvy was eradicated when the British Royal Navy started following the advice of James Lind, who said eating a few lemons could prevent and even cure the dreaded disease. The Vikings found allies for their restrictive views in Brazil, Indonesia, Thailand, Benin, Malaysia, and Nigeria.

In view of such widespread discord, the Chairman of the Committee could not but concede defeat and propose that the guideline should "remain on step three" of the eight-step approval procedure. He invited governments once again to make written comments on the draft text before, one year from now, the Committee will consider the matter anew. Unfortunately, or should we say fortunately, there was no time left to continue discussions.

In conclusion, and in a more than one sense, consumers and the health food industry as well as natural medicine were "saved by the bell." What remains to be done is a lot of education on the beneficial and indeed life saving character of nutritional supplementation. While a year may seem to be a long time to some, there is great urgency to act.

Codex, Globalization, and the
Pharmaceutical Monopoly on Health

The issue should also be examined in a broader context. Codex Alimentarius and its proposed guidelines are but the tip of the proverbial iceberg. The discussions mirror the deadly embrace of two giants - global pharmaceutical and food industries allied with "western medicine" on the one hand and the age-old traditions of herbalism and "traditional medicine" with the more recently developed nutritional approach of "cellular medicine" on the other. Clearly, the Codex issue cannot resolve until there is a recognition of the fact that medicine must not be monopolized by any one particular system.

We need to approach health from a viewpoint of plurality, and that includes abandoning the currently widespread insistence of western governments that "foods must not be used to cure or prevent any disease." Codex cannot escape its responsibilities for our health by saying "we deal only in foods," or, put into different words, "medicine is none of our business." A balance must be struck between prevention based on nutrition and traditional means on one side and the pharmaceutical approach to health on the other.

Globalization of health care under the domination of our particular brand of pharmaceutically dominated "scientific western medicine" will inevitably lead to a broadening of the conflict we observe in these discussions. Insistence on a pharma-centered approach to health has turned out to be so wasteful that governments are now unable to bear its costs. The system is breaking down, western populations are killed by diet-related scourges such as heart disease and cancer, while the use of supplements for preventive purposes is officially frowned upon. At the same time, properly approved and prescribed pharmaceutical drugs have become the third or fourth most widespread cause of death in the "civilized" nations.

What to Do?

The forces proposing a pluralistic approach to health must wake up and start working together. Time is short. One year, the time that will pass before this particular Codex Committee is to meet again, is nothing in the time scale of legislative developments. For the sake of our health we should advocate our right to choose – loudly if needed – to eat real food, preferably organic, to use nutrients for prevention and to return to scientific medicinal traditions that have stood the test of millennia and have served us well. We must combine these age-old scientific traditions with new research and knowledge of biochemistry; but we should also be wary of "scientific adventures" such as genetic modification of our foods, the invention of ever new "xeno-biotic" drugs, and the poisoning of our environment in the name of "pest control" and "weed killing."

Let's get to work to build a great alliance. Codex is the spark, but the real prize is our health, if not the survival of our children and of future generations.

We all have a better guide in ourselves, if we would attend to it, than any other person can be.
- Jane Austen, Mansfield Park

Report From the Eastern Front:
Author finds much to mistrust at recent Codex session in Berlin

By Scott C. Tips

(November 2002 Codex Meeting)

(Published in *Whole Foods Magazine*, January 2003)

One and a quarter hours! My flight from Zurich to Berlin took longer than that. Yet, that was all the time allotted by the chairman of the Codex Alimentarius Committee on Nutrition and Foods for Special Dietary Uses at this 24th session in Berlin, Germany for discussing the numerous standards that Codex wants to impose on vitamin and mineral supplements. The chairman's and most delegates' "dreamlist" includes maximum and minimum potencies for supplements, a "positive" list denoting those supplements permitted to be sold, and a "negative" list of prohibited supplements. These are the basic top-down, control-freak, bureaucratic mindset-driven types of rules and regulations that stifle progress and result in needless human suffering and deaths. Fortunately, due to the shortage of time, virtually no progress was made at this meeting and health freedom was the temporary winner.

To be fair, at last year's session, the infant-formula topics had been badly short-changed in favor of the discussion on dietary supplements. This year, it was vitamin and mineral supplements' turn in the backseat. Nevertheless, there were important developments. But first some background.

Credentials Denied

Unlike in previous years, I was not a member of the United States delegation at this meeting. Due to other commitments, I had submitted my application too late to the United States Codex office to be automatically admitted to the delegation; and, unlike last year when Dr. Elizabeth Yetley (the official U.S. delegate) waived me onto the delegation, she refused to permit me to be a member this year. Perhaps my criticism of her failure to follow U.S. law or to advocate freedom at the last meeting was an important factor in her refusal. Regardless of the reasons, she was not saying why she would not let me on this year when she had last time. No matter. I had already applied to the Codex Alimentarius Committee for International Non Governmental Organization (INGO) seeking observer status for my client, the National Health Federation ("NHF"). Such status would grant it a seat at the meeting and the right to present its views if called upon by the chairman. Although Codex initially refused to grant NHF this observer status, I repeatedly persisted until they had agreed with my arguments that NHF deserved to be an INGO at the upcoming meeting, then a bare two weeks away.

Keep in mind that members of the U.S. delegation are forbidden from lobbying other official delegates on Codex issues. INGOs, on the other hand, are not prohibited from doing any lobbying. So, thank God that I had not been admitted onto the U.S. delegation (as I had wanted) but did obtain INGO status for the NHF. In that way, I could both speak out at the meeting and lobby other delegates without restriction. After all, to my knowledge, there were no other INGO lobbying Codex delegates in favor of health freedom. And there was certainly no other INGO who spoke out in favor of health freedom either.

Surprisingly, one government delegate did advocate health freedom and the beneficial effects of dietary supplements: Mrs. Antoinette Booyzen of South Africa. Mrs. Booyzen, who has herself personally witnessed the substantial beneficial health effects of dietary supplements, had the courage to defy all other delegates' mindless position that supplements are only good to prevent deficiencies. In an opening statement, she told the other delegates exactly what they needed to hear - that overwhelming evidence exists that vitamin supplements are important and necessary for optimum nutrition and to prevent diseases. Only the NHF spoke up to support the South African position.

Mrs. Booyzen then proposed a new preamble to the Codex standards that recognized dietary supplements as important in preventing and reducing the risk of disease. All other delegations, such as Denmark, our old "favorite" Norway, and Brazil, who spoke denigrated this position. Germany even called South Africa's proposed change procedurally incorrect because it had not been submitted in writing first. Because the chairman, who is German, always defers to the German delegate's stated position (I have never seen him act contrary to any position stated by the German delegate), the proposed South African change to the preamble was promptly deleted from the overhead screen used to show Codex language changes. Although I repeatedly requested recognition by the chairman to speak out in support of South Africa's proposed new preamble, the chairman flatly refused to call on me and I had to suffer the other delegations' ignorant remarks in silence.

The U.S. delegate, Dr. Yetley, never stated support for the South African position. However, she did at least advocate certain language changes within the Codex document to clarify that the Codex standards were only guidelines and not requirements. The official U.S. position was that the mandatory verb "shall" should be replaced by the subjunctive-verb tense "should" in order to reflect the "voluntary" nature of Codex standards. On behalf of the NHF, I spoke out in favor of this U.S. position, although I do not think it alone would protect consumers from harsh Codex standards. I rather suspect that the U.S. position in this regard was influenced in large part by the persistent inquiries and comments of Suzan Walter, president of the American Holistic Health Association, who has repeatedly demanded of both the Food and Drug Administration (FDA) and Codex to specify whether Codex standards are guidelines or mandates.

Name's Not the Same

The European Union's delegate proposed a change in the title of the Codex standards to add the word "food" so that the title would now read "Proposed Draft Guidelines for Vitamins and Mineral Food Supplements." Although this change was never voted upon, the chairman unilaterally decided that it was appropriate and it became de facto the new title. The EU delegate obviously did not want vitamins and minerals for food use to be confused with those vitamins and minerals restricted by the dictatorial European rules on vitamin and mineral drugs (such as "overpotent" vitamin C).

The all-too-slick way in which the Codex document title wa changed without a vote, though, illustrates the truly dangerou nature of these world organizations. Although on the surface seem ingly noble and egalitarian, they are really composed of unelectec government bureaucrats who make fundamentally important deci sions about rules and regulations that govern our lives and ou health. These bureaucrats would not know true freedom if it walkec up and bit them on their collective noses. And the slick manner ir which the Codex title was changed simply because two men agreec that it should be changed shows how easily far-reaching decision: affecting our lives (and those of millions and billions of others) are made with no real checks and balances.

The chairman then quickly moved on to his favorite topic setting maximum limits on vitamins and minerals. As before, the delegates essentially divided into two camps: those who supportec maximum limits that should not exceed 100% of the Recommended Dietary Intake levels and those who supportec more liberal maximum limits based upon "scientific" risk assess ment. The second, "scientific risk assessment" camp was itself divided into a more restrictive European Union version of risk assessment and a U.S.-led version of risk-assessment that was more industry oriented. After some discussion, it became clear that the RDI camp had lost a great number of proponents with the United States gaining support from, of all countries, Switzerland and Peru. Still stuck in the Middle Ages, Norway, Brazil and Malaysia stood by their fear of vitamins and minerals by espousing 100% RDI lim its on vitamins and minerals.

I was finally once again recognized by the chairman and told the delegates that scientific evidence demonstrated that vitamins and minerals were inherently safe and that, in fact, more persons had died at the hands of doctors than from vitamins or minerals. I suggested that if they wanted to entertain upper limits on anything, then they should place upper limits on hospital stays. The chair man, obviously displeased with my comments, interrupted me.

Interestingly enough, when discussing infant cereals, Dr. Yetley had, herself, previously provided support for the NHF position when she stated, "There should be no upper limit for fiber because there is no adverse effect." Her comment was certainly true and certainly applicable to vitamin and mineral supplements as well. Perhaps at next year's meeting she will expand her position to include supplements.

The Codex session on vitamins and minerals ended rather abruptly at 8:30 p.m. amidst chairman-generated confusion as to whether the Committee would continue the next morning in a special session. The delegates almost uniformly objected and, so, after spending only a little more than one hour on the issue of vitamins and minerals, the Committee deferred the topic for the next year.

Because of some internal structural changes in the German host organization, there are rumors that both the chairman and the city location will be different next year. Some have predicted that next year's meeting will be held in Bonn, Germany instead of in Berlin and that Dr. Rolf Grossklaus, who is definitely not liked by many delegates, will be replaced by another German technocrat. Time will tell.

How Much Freedom?

In the meantime, though, what is clear is that the momentum has shifted away from very restrictive limits on vitamin and mineral potencies to more liberal limits. While some, such as the Council for Responsible Nutrition (CRN), seem to think that risk-assessment based limits will mean no limits in many cases, I am not so trusting of orthodox science. Remember, these are the same men and women who think that niacin flushing is a deleterious effect that requires potency limits on niacin! Besides, what kind of person can accept and be comfortable with any kinds of chains? It's like saying that we should accept a curfew of 10 p.m. because it is so much better than one of 7 p.m.

My own prediction is that the Codex Alimentarius process will take so long that it will only briefly take effect or else be discarded into the dustbin of history as major historical events such as war, resurgent nationalism, and trade protectionism overtake it. Unfortunately, the obvious alternative of an international free market in dietary supplements that lets the consumer freely choose for himself or herself what to put into his or her own body is not seriously discussed or considered. Yet, such freedom, as it always has been, is the best way to health and prosperity.

Liberty is meaningless if it is only the liberty to agree with those in power.
- Ludwig von Mises

Rearranging the Deck Chairs on the Titanic

By Scott C. Tips

(Published in *Whole Foods Magazine*, January 2004)

Some observant person once noted "Amateurs built the Ark, professionals built the Titanic." Well, after attending the recent Codex Alimentarius committee meeting in Bonn, Germany last November, I could see that the professionals were at it again. The beautiful Indian summer weather in Bonn must have lifted their spirits because the professionals spent an energetic week busily greasing the skids to launch their Titanic into the water.

Of course, as you recall, Codex Alimentarius is an international body guided by the World Health Organization and the Food and Agriculture Organization of the United Nations and charged with establishing international trade standards for foods. The food standards that it establishes are backed by the power of the World Trade Organization (WTO), which settles trade disputes between nations by ruling upon complaints and then levying punitive fines upon the offending country. The WTO's rulings have caused countries, including the United States, to change its domestic laws in order to comply with WTO rulings. Within Codex Alimentarius there are various committees that deal with specific food issues. My focus has been on the Codex Committee on Nutrition and Foods for Special Dietary Uses, which, among other things, has spent several decades inching forward in its efforts to finalize its *Guidelines for Vitamin and Mineral Supplements*. Once completed, however, this document will be the basis by which food-supplement standards will be measured everywhere. And like the Titanic, it is a disaster waiting to happen.

For the fourth year in a row, I was there as a delegate. Thanks once again to the National Health Federation (NHF)(www.then-hf.com), the nonprofit consumer health-freedom organization for whom I obtained Codex observer status beginning with the 2002 meeting, my travel and hotel expenses were covered. I was also very ably assisted on the delegation by Tamara Thérèsa Mosegaard of MayDay and Paul Anthony Taylor from the United Kingdom. Together, we did our best to stem the anti-freedom tide; but, unfortunately, the NHF was the only consistently pro-health freedom voice at the Codex meeting.

As the country host for the Committee meeting, Germany provided both the location and the chairman. It also provided the most attendees. The chairman again this year was the irrepressible Dr. Rolf Grossklaus, who (presumably under some pressure from his superiors, the "High Command") ran the meeting more efficiently this year than in the previous years of my attendance. It is important to remember that, with almost fifty countries and more than thirty nongovernmental organizations represented, there is no voting at these meetings. Dr. Grossklaus sits at the head table and arbitrates the discussions using a procedure sweetly called "consensus." When he decides that the subject has been adequately discussed, he then announces what the consensus is and moves on to the next agenda item. Sometimes, rarely actually, there are murmurs of disapproval if Dr. Grossklaus' decision does not track reality; but most often there are no expressions of disagreement. Either way, consensus is "reached" and the discussion on the next topic starts.

"What the EU Wants, the EU Gets"

Not surprisingly, in finding consensus, this German chairman consistently and unerringly rules in favor of the representative for the European Union (EU). Time after time, I noticed that the Chairman adopted as the consensus decision the very position taken by the EU representative. When Malaysia wanted to change the title of the Guidelines by deleting the word "food," the EU objected. Dr. Grossklaus agreed with the EU. When South Africa tried to amend the Preamble to the Guidelines to include a statement that vitamins and minerals aid in the prevention of chronic diseases, the EU objected that food and prevention could not go together. Dr. Grossklaus agreed with the EU. When the EU announced that it wanted to make sure that all food supplements (not just vitamins and minerals) would be covered by the Codex restrictions, Dr. Grossklaus agreed to the EU's proposed wording. When the EU decided that the definition of vitamin and mineral food supplements should be modified by tacking on the words "designed to be taken as small unit quantities," Dr. Grossklaus agreed. When the United States, with much support from others, wanted to add wording that vitamins and minerals could be from both natural and synthetic sources, the EU objected and asked that the language be placed in brackets, indicating the language was not approved but must run the gauntlet of approval again next year. Dr. Grossklaus put the language in brackets. When the EU and the United States argued on the same side against retaining the RDA upper limits on vitamins, Dr. Grossklaus found consensus with the EU and United States position. Yet, when the EU objected to the United States' and many other delegates' (including the NHF's) position that the Committee should delete the restrictive wording that "When the maximum levels are set, due account should be taken to the reference intake values of vitamins and minerals for the population," Dr. Grossklaus agreed with the EU and retained the sentence. When various delegations (South Africa, IADSA, and the NHF) objected to language that would require vitamin and mineral supplements to be "named" as "food supplements" and suggested instead alternative wording that would distinguish the need to label the product as a "food supplement" from the actual product name, the EU disagreed. Dr. Grossklaus sided with the EU. When the EU and the United States were again at odds over whether or not the amount of vitamins and minerals contained in a product should be disclosed by the inane and useless European bulk-product system of stating so-much weight of a product yields so-many milligrams or micrograms of vitamins and minerals (leaving the hapless consumer to do the math to figure out how much is in each capsule or tablet) or be disclosed by the more direct American way of stating the milligram and microgram quantity of the vitamins and minerals per capsule or tablet, Dr. Grossklaus once again decided in favor of the EU, although he did permit the American suggested wording to remain in the sentence in the brackets that indicate it must be reviewed again next year.

By this point, I was so disgusted with the Chairman's pattern of rubber-stamping as "consensus" the EU representative's opinion, that, when called upon to speak, I told the Chairman that he was just fashioning the Guideline to whatever the EU wanted. "What the EU wants, the EU gets," I told him and the others, adding that there was no consensus at all in favor of the EU position. I was not surprised, though, to find that no other delegation verbally supported me on this. And Dr. Grossklaus, looking down on the group from his judge's chair, brushed aside my remarks with an unimpressive "I reject your comment as untrue." And the charade continued with subsequent EU wording suggestions of course getting Dr. Grossklaus' fair nod.

At one time, unknowingly contradicting what he would later tell me in rejecting my complaint of favoritism, Dr. Grossklaus justified his favoring of the EU by stating that the EU represented 15 countries, as if that faint logic made any sort of difference. Why was Dr. Grossklaus counting countries that joined together into a federal union? What about the fifty states of the United States? What about China with a far greater population than the EU? Or India? Perhaps, expanding upon Dr. Grossklaus' logic, he should weight his decisions instead in favor of the Chinese or Indian positions since they are the most populous countries of all. But, no, Dr. Grossklaus is a citizen of Germany, a member state of the EU. We know where his sympathies lie, as well as where his instructions must come from.

South Africa Shines

True to her word given at the end of the 2002 Committee meeting, South African delegate Antoinette Booyzen introduced at this most recent meeting certain Preamble and other language in an attempt to avoid the restrictive tone of the Guidelines sought by many other delegates. Her proposed amendment to the Preamble of the Guidelines would have had Codex endorsing people to "select a healthy diet and supplement this diet with those nutrients for which the intake from the diet is insufficient to meet the requirements necessary for the prevention of chronic diseases and/or for the promotion of health beyond the demands of preventing micronutrient deficiencies." Knowing that this wording would be proposed, I had asked Elizabeth Yetley, the head of the U.S. delegation, to support South Africa's proposed wording; but she declined, saying that it was a losing cause. So, when the matter came up for discussion, only the NHF and the Council for Responsible Nutrition supported South Africa's proposal. On this occasion as on many others, I repeatedly slugged it out verbally with the EU representative, who claimed to speak for the EU consumer. It was a lonely fight.

Not deterred by the EU, Mrs. Booyzen was more verbal at this year's meeting than the previous one and did not shy away from controversy. Unfortunately, the tag team of the Chairman and the EU representative effectively throttled any progress away from controls and restrictions and the mainstream view that vitamins and minerals are only there to prevent deficiencies.

The Chains Are Loosened

Press releases from supplement-industry organizations have trumpeted the "victory" of the recent session's deletion of Upper Limits on vitamins and minerals based on the insanely low Recommended Daily Allowances (RDAs). In a limited sense the claim of victory is true – Upper Limits based upon RDAs would have been horribly restrictive. But in rushing towards looser restrictions based on the false security of "scientific risk assessment," they are only substituting looser handcuffs for tight ones. Proponents of the "scientific risk assessment" method of establishing safe Upper Limits for vitamins and minerals think that the (expensive) studies that will be done, and that have been done, will show that the limits should be set high, even very high. I sincerely hope that they are right.

Unfortunately, recent events are more supportive of the fears of those of my jaded health-freedom colleagues who note that the EU Scientific Committee on Food has used "scientific risk assessment" to establish ridiculously low upper intake levels for niacin (10 mg.) and for Vitamin B6 (25 mg.). This supports what I have argued for years: Science is not some objective standard these days (if it ever were), it is a tool that can be shaped to support whatever argument or position its users want. If researchers want to argue that Vitamin C is dangerous above a certain level, then they will find or create "scientific" studies that support their position. They have done this in the past, they are doing it now with the EU Scientific

Committee on Food, and they are doing it through numerous false studies that are published almost monthly in the common press to frighten consumers away from dietary supplements. So-called scientific risk assessment is a trap.

So, yes, the severe Upper Limits that would have plagued us had the RDAs become the standard are gone; but there are still Upper Limits being set on natural substances that actually do not even require upper limits at all. All of this time, energy, and money is being wasted to set standards that are unnecessary as they are currently being framed. After all, do we set Upper Limits on water, fiber, or food? So while we can all breathe a sigh of relief that we have avoided the electric chair, we should not sing too loudly as we are led into the prison cell that will become our home for the rest of our lives.

The Future

In their eagerness to help us, the professionals are determined to ruin our health and our lives. They are constructing this grand edifice of health standards to protect us from what they see as fraudulent and potentially dangerous health supplements. With their pharmaceutical mindset, it is not difficult to perceive how these proponents of control might view vitamins and minerals as dangerous – either to health or to their pocketbooks. Others ascribe an even more sinister motive to these professionals, seeing them as the tools and agents of the pharmaceutical industry that want to hijack the dietary-supplement industry and thereby keep it from ever really competing with the medicines of death that they sell.

Regardless, while we are riding on this voyage of regulatory discovery, it is increasingly apparent that we are all at best simply rearranging the deck chairs on this Titanic. Unless this Behemoth changes course radically, and soon, many lives will be lost. Education, political action, lawsuits, and coordinated efforts by health-freedom lovers are all important. Each of us must do whatever we can to stop the onward rush of this ship to disaster.

Important News from Bonn

By Suzan Walter

Report from Suzan Walter, president of American Holistic Health Association, on her attendance at the November 3-7, 2003, session of Codex Committee on Nutrition and Foods for Special Dietary Uses (CCNFSDU) in Bonn, Germany.

A decade of polarized debate quietly came to an end on November 3, 2003. A major decision impacting international trade of nutritional supplements was made to use upper safe limits as the maximum allowed levels for vitamin-and-mineral food supplements. It was decided that sound scientific research using proper risk-assessment protocols will establish at what point a nutrient becomes toxic or harmful. To protect the consumer, vitamin-and-mineral food supplement products are to be restricted to stay below this upper safe limit.

The alternative option would have set these maximum levels at a significantly lower level of 100% of the recommended daily amounts (RDA). Delegates who were against this option envisioned a future with supplement products restricted to very low levels of potency. We can breathe easier that this option was defeated.

Why should you care? Because this decision was made by the Codex Alimentarius, a body charged with drafting international trade standards for foods. These standards are used by the World Trade Organization (WTO) in settling trade disputes between countries. If a country should lose an international dispute, the WTO can use powerful economic trade sanctions to pressure a country to change its laws and actions. If you are a consumer of vitamin and mineral supplements, we encourage you to be vigilant for any potential threat from external sources that might weaken the current U.S. regulations that allow you open access to nutritional supplement products.

For now, be reassured that the decision not to use RDAs as the maximum upper limits removed a possible serious threat.

Since Codex is seldom mentioned in the U.S. media, those new to Codex may wish to visit codexinfo.org for an overview of Codex Alimentarius and an explanation of the role of the Codex Committee on Nutrition and Foods for Special Dietary Uses (CCNFSDU). This committee is the group responsible for drafting the Guidelines for Vitamin and Mineral Food Supplements. Check out both Pro and Con viewpoints and decide for yourself if you wish to continue to track the development of the Guidelines.

Are you interested in learning more about what happened at the CCNFSDU session in Bonn, Germany, held during the first week in November 2003? As Codex sessions do not publish detailed minutes, only very limited summary reports, I offer below my personal observations of the discussions and decisions related to the Guidelines.

My overall impression is that the 2003 CCNFSDU session was well run and productive. When compared to the session in 2002 when very little progress was made and the delegates were ready to lynch the chair for his seeming unfair and ineffective leadership, this is a significant improvement. This year the chair, Dr. Rolf Grossklaus, followed the Codex procedures for allowing comments from delegates, acknowledging written comments submitted prior to the session, summarizing general consensus, and facilitating compromises. Whereas in 2002 he allowed one agenda item to consume most of the three days allotted for discussion, this year the chair did an admirable job of allotting sufficient time for each of 13 agenda items. On several occasions this year there was applause from the 230 delegates at the completion of addressing an agenda item. This was to acknowledge that despite the divergent positions among the 48 country and 31 international non-government organization (NGO) delegations, significant progress had been made.

Not that all delegates were totally happy with the chair's actions. The Codex procedure to use consensus (as perceived by the chair) rather than voting, takes some getting used to by those of us accustomed to democratic proceedings. Consensus can be very subjective, and on occasion some delegates did voice their view that the chair was favoring the European Community (EC) delegate's positions. In defense, the chair pointed out that this one individual was representing 15 European Union countries. You can review the report below and decide for yourself.

My main interest for attending the CCNFSDU session was for Agenda Item #5, the *Guidelines for Vitamin and Mineral Food Supplements*. A copy of this document is available on-line. I recommend that you access the document and follow along as I move from section to section. The document shows the status of the *Guidelines* after the changes made at the 2003 CCNFSDU session. New words are underlined. Words removed are crossed out. Square brackets indicate that the words within the brackets are not finalized and will be debated at a future committee session.

On Monday, November 3, the session reached Agenda Item #5. The chair announced that his main goal in this session was to address the areas in the *Guidelines* document that were still in square brackets and finalize as many as possible.

Even with this goal, the first item brought up was not in square brackets. It was the word "Food" in the Title: *Guidelines for Vitamin and Mineral Food Supplements*. This word had been added at the 2002 session at the request of the EC. Malaysia, South Africa, and India voiced support for removing this word. The EC supported retaining the word. South Africa suggested an alternative "Vitamin and Mineral Supplements Regulated as Foods." There was further discussion, including the chair's comment that the committee only deals with foods. Finally, the chair ended discussion on this topic, and announced that the word "Food" would not be removed. Throughout the Guidelines text, whenever the phrase, "vitamin and mineral supplements," appeared it would be changed to "vitamin and mineral food supplements."

Next, South Africa suggested revised wording for the *Preamble* to add mention of the role of vitamins and minerals in the prevention of chronic diseases. Since the Food and Agricultural Organization of the United Nation's World Health Organization (FAO/WHO) publication, "Diet, Nutrition and the Prevention of Chronic Diseases," was being distributed at the CCNFSDU session, it was assumed this premise would be an easy sell. The National Health Federation (NHF) spoke in support of the South African suggestion. When, the EC delegate took the floor, he insisted that food and prevention did not go together. The chair commented that medicines are for prevention and treatment of diseases, whereas food supplements are to maintain health. There was continued discussion, with the key point being that Codex regulations prohibited claims that food prevents disease. The chair declared that the Preamble would not be revised.

Under the 1. *Scope* section of the Guidelines, there was debate about a section dealing with jurisdictions and which countries would be under the authority of the *Guidelines*. The wording was ultimately condensed by deleting the first sentence and leaving the second sentence, which states that the *Guidelines* were limited to countries regulating vitamin and mineral supplements as foods.

Mixed in with this discussion was consideration of an EC request to expand the wording to include food supplements containing other ingredients (in addition to vitamins and minerals). This request was motivated by a concern that the addition of an extra ingredient might be a technicality to keep a product from being required to abide by the *Guidelines*. The EC was successful and the following was added: "Food supplements containing vitamins and/or minerals as well as other ingredients should also be in conformity with the specific rules on vitamins and minerals laid down in these Guidelines."

Under the 2. *Definitions* section the focus was on deleting a sentence related to the use of supplements. The sentence in question included the text, "intake from food is insufficient or where the consumers consider their diet requires supplementation." New Zealand, Thailand, Tunisia, and Kenya supported removing the sentence. Malaysia and India voiced support for keeping the sentence. The chair declared consensus that the sentence would be removed as the content was covered in the Preamble.

The Definitions discussion continued as the EC lobbied to add the wording, "marketed in dose form" and "designed to be taken in measured small unit quantities," to ensure that supplements were not confused with conventional food. The U.S. pointed out that "dose" was related to drugs in the U.S. and that "small unit" was confusing. Many countries (including the U.S., South Africa, Nigeria, Philippines, and India) supported not adding the "small measured unit quantities" wording. It was noted that the current text, "capsules, tablets, powders, solutions, etc., not in conventional food form," was sufficient to make this point clear. The EC position was supported by Germany and France (who are members of the EC). The chair declared that the EC statement, "They are designed to be taken as measured [small unit quantities]," would be added to Guidelines. (Remember that Codex text in square brackets means that this wording is not finalized and will be debated at a future session.)

In the 3. *Composition* section, there was significant support for the suggestion by the U.S. to clarify in 3.1.2 that vitamins and minerals could be from both "natural and synthetic" sources. However, this addition was put into square brackets at the request of the EC. The need to clarify the criteria for sources for purity resulted in several other additions.

The U.S. request to delete 3.1.3 was quietly declared a group consensus on the basis that the Codex risk-assessment guidelines covered this safety issue.

Section 3.2 *Contents of Vitamins and Minerals* contains the minimum and maximum levels - the hot topics!

Section 3.2.1 sets the minimum level of each vitamin and/or mineral contained in a supplement product. Up to now, the amounts 15% and 33% were in square brackets, meaning that the committee needed to pick. My notes show that the U.S., Malaysia, and South Africa spoke out to support 15%. Japan, India, Thailand, and Switzerland felt this was too low. The chair declared that the 15% had the majority and that 15% corresponded to the value for "source" in the Guidelines for Use of Nutrition Claims and a higher value might create practical difficulties for certain nutrients.

Next we arrived at Section 3.2.2, dealing with maximum levels. For years this has been the most dramatically debated section of the *Guidelines*. The two widely divergent options are about what will be the criteria for setting maximum levels.

"*For maximum level of each vitamin and/or mineral contained in a vitamin and mineral supplement per daily portion of consumption as suggested by the manufacturer*

(Option #1) should not exceed [100%] of the recommended daily intake as determined by FAO/WHO.
OR
(Option #2) shall be set taking the following criteria into account:

    (a) upper safe levels of vitamins and mineral established by scientific risk assessment based on generally accepted scientific data, taking into consideration, as appropriate, the varying degrees of sensitivity of different consumer groups;
    (b) the daily intake of vitamins and minerals from other dietary sources.

When the maximum levels are set, due account should be taken to the reference intake values of vitamins and minerals for the population."

My notes show that this year Norway, Malaysia, and Thailand spoke in support of the first option. The EC, South Africa, Japan, the U.S., and Switzerland spoke in support of the second option. The chair declared consensus in support of the second option, with the final report to record that Norway, Malaysia, and Thailand did not agree. (Later, Brazil requested to go on record that its written comments supported the first option.) Thus, after years and years of heated debate, this important issue was quietly decided and the session moved on. Amazing.

Next, the discussion was on the final sentence under Option #2, "When the maximum levels are set, due account should be taken to the reference intake values of vitamins and minerals for the population." The U.S., Tunisia, the International Alliance of Dietary/Food Supplement Association (IADSA), New Zealand, Philippines, South Africa, the Council for Responsible Nutrition (CRN), and the National Health Federation (NHF) spoke in support of deleting this sentence. The EC, Norway, and Italy spoke in support of retaining this sentence. The chair decided to keep this sentence, but retain it in square brackets for further discussion at a future session.

On Tuesday, November 4, the session continued with Agenda Item #5. Section 4. *Packaging*, was skipped over, as it did not have any text in square brackets. The final section 5. *Labeling*, which included square brackets in 5.2 - 5.5 and 5.8 - 5.9, received considerable attention.

Under 5.2, the need for the "name of the product" was hotly debated. The IADSA and South Africa noted that any product label will indicate the contents and adding "vitamin and mineral supplement" was not needed. The chair quoted from *Codex Procedural Manual*, page 95, that the label must have the "name of the food." After much discussion, the compromise was to change the wording to "The name of the product shall be 'food supplement' with an indication of the category(ies) of nutrients or of the individual vitamin(s) and/or mineral(s) contained in the product as the case may be."

5.3 was finalized (removed from square brackets) with some minor revisions.

The discussion on 5.4 was most interesting. Although the EC was open to removing the "dose" reference, the various ways amounts of a nutrient could be presented on a label immediately came into contention. There could be the amount per portion of the product recommended for daily consumption (such as three units of the product provide the recommended daily intake of nutrient listed on the label). There could also be the amount per single unit of the product (such as amount of nutrient per tablet or capsule in the container). Do consumers need to be able to determine how many units are needed to reach the amount they wish to take, or will they be forced to do the math? Consensus could not be reached. One option was finalized and the second placed within square brackets. Again, the EC and the U.S. were on opposing sides of the debate, with the U.S. and NHF supporting the single-use information that makes it easier for consumers to calculate the amount they desire.

In this discussion, the U.S. succeeded in changing "shall" to "should" throughout the document, as appropriate, to be in keeping with the intent that this is to be suggested guidelines. (Note: This ignores the fact that WTO does not differentiate between standards and guidelines and uses both as standards.)

Section 5.5 includes text stating that labeling is to be in terms of "reference values." Some delegates pointed out that current Nutrient Reference Values (NRVs) are based on a 1988 Helsink Consultation and are thus incomplete and outdated. The idea would be to have FAO/WHO fund an expert consultation for these updates. However, current FAO/WHO budgeting problems would prevent this from happening for quite some time. The committee decided to do what was within their jurisdiction: establish an electronic working group made up of members of CCNFSDU delegations. Leadership of this working group needs to be a country. The U.S., Germany and the EC were invited, but each felt it was unable to accept. Non-government organizations NHF and CRN were willing to assist, once a lead country was established. No country stepped forward. Later in the session, however, South Africa accepted the leadership of this important assignment. All delegations were invited to submit proposals for inclusion in this project. While the current NRVs are based on statistics combining men and women, the committee voiced the opinion that separate values needed to be established by gender, age (children and seniors), and special needs groups (pregnant women and nursing mothers). The working group is to compile all into a document of revised NRVs for consideration at the 2004 CCNFSDU session.

The discussion on 5.7 was whether or not a warning statement is needed on supplement labels. Arguments to delete this requirement were based on the fact that products would be safe because of the 3.2.2 upper safe limits criteria. Another argument noted that too much data on a label might dilute its impact. The U.S., CRN, and NHF supported deleting 5.7. The EC did not. A compromise was reached that instead of a warning there would be a recommendation not to exceed the maximum one-day amount.

Under 5.8. there were strong feelings about wording on a label about supplements might be used in place of a meal. The EC supported a mandatory statement that food supplements should not be used as a substitute for a varied diet. The U.S. supported the position that no statement on the label should imply that supplements be used to replace a meal or a varied diet. This would remove an additional required statement on the label. China supported deleting 5.8 entirely. A compromise statement similar to what the U.S. proposed received consensus.

The 5.9 text that the label must include a statement that supplements should be taken on the advice of a nutritionist, dietitian, or medical doctor has generated heated debate in past years. This year, after very little discussion, the chair declared general consensus to delete 5.9. It was noted that Philippines and Malaysia did not support this consensus.

At this point in the session, all square brackets for Agenda Item #5 had been addressed. Now the chair allowed delegates to bring up issues regarding other sections of the *Guidelines*.

The EC brought up 4.3 in the Packaging section. This text required child-resistant packaging. They recommended deleting 4.3 and substituting a statement that the label must contain a statement that product should be stored out of the reach of young children. Many countries supported the EC. One of the arguments pointed out the difficulty senior citizens have in opening the child-resistant packaging. The chair declared consensus, 4.3 was deleted, and the new statement added as a new 5.9 under Labeling.

Next, South Africa brought up 3.2.3 and suggested additional wording to stop regulatory authorities from making unscientific barriers to trade. The chair felt this was redundant. Then the EC questioned the levels referenced and recommended deleting 3.2.3. The chair declared that 3.2.3 would be deleted. (Note: Prior written comments by the U.S. supported deleting 3.2.3 as no longer necessary with the approval of 3.2.2.)

This concluded committee revisions of the Guidelines at this session. The chair declared that significant progress had been made and the document was to move from Step 3 to Step 5 (Note: There are eight steps before final approval of a standard by the Codex Alimentarius Commission (CAC) and availability for official use. Once a text is close to its final form, it is set at Step 5 and submitted to the CAC for initial feedback.).

The chair moved on to the next agenda item. The CCNFSDU session continued.

The significant progress made this year was in sharp contrast to the ineffective 35 minutes of debate in 2002. Delegates could feel very proud of what they accomplished in 2003.

Distrust all in whom the impulse to punish is powerful.
- Friedrich Wilhelm Nietzsche

A Meeting of Two

By Scott C. Tips

(Published in *Health Freedom News*, Vol. 22, No 4, Winter 2004)

The most recent meeting of the 26th session of the Codex Committee on Nutrition and Foods for Special Dietary Uses was held during the first week of November 2004, in Bonn, Germany; and some 280 people dutifully sat in chairs, listened, and watched. A few of them even occasionally spoke up, mostly in agreement with the Gang of Two, the European Commission (EU) Representative Basil Mathioudakis and his sidekick, the Committee Chairman Dr. Ralf Grossklaus. Some few others quibbled over details. An even fewer number of us, which you could count on one hand and have fingers left over, fought and argued back. But to paraphrase Groucho Marx, "I had a perfectly wonderful week, but this wasn't it." Read on and you will see why.

Meet the Codex Alimentarius Commission.

For those of you new to the game, the Codex Alimentarius Commission is an international body establishing global trade standards for foods. Sponsored jointly by the World Health Organization and the Food and Agriculture Organization of the United Nations, it has various committees dealing with specific food issues. And each committee is hosted in turn by a particular country that provides the chairman and the meeting place in that country.

The committee concerned with food supplements is the Codex Committee on Nutrition and Foods for Special Dietary Uses, which is hosted by Germany and meets in Bonn every November. This particular committee is important to you because it is establishing "guidelines" that will govern the international trade in vitamins and minerals. And, in my opinion, these euphemistically called "guidelines" will be used not only to exclude superior American dietary supplements from the European marketplace but they will also be used, either directly or by way of example, to stifle the domestic American market in supplements as well.

Meet the National Health Federation.

That is precisely why the National Health Federation (NHF) (www.thenhf.com), a nonprofit consumer health-freedom organization, has been sending me to these Codex committee meetings every year for five years in a row now. Having obtained official Codex observer status, the NHF is able to attend and speak out (when the Chairman chooses to recognize it) at these meetings. It is also able to, and did, submit written arguments in favor of health-freedom positions at these meetings.

Fortunately, as the NHF delegate, I was ably assisted by Paul Anthony Taylor, an NHF Board member, and Sepp Hasslberger, an NHF Advisory Board member. Also extremely helpful were attendees Tamara Thérèsa Mosegaard of Danish-based MayDay International as well as Peter Helgason and Dr. Carolyn Dean of the Canadian-based Friends of Freedom group. Paul Taylor, in particular, had drafted some very thorough position papers promoting free access to vitamins and minerals as well as realistic Nutrient Reference Values that the NHF submitted to the Committee to promote a scientific pro-health-freedom view.

We Were Delegates Once and Young.

The meeting began innocuously enough on Monday morning in a large meeting hall on the banks of the tellingly swiftly-flowing Rhine. The Agenda was first considered and adopted with one small alteration in the order of items to be discussed. Then, the initial agenda items were covered so quickly that, by mid-afternoon, the Committee had already arrived at Agenda Item No. 4, the controversial *Draft Guidelines for Vitamin and Mineral Food Supplements.*

The Chairman, Dr. Grossklaus, began the discussion of this Agenda item by peremptorily announcing that the Committee would only consider the few, remaining sentences and words in the draft Guidelines that were enclosed in brackets. Nothing else was to be considered or discussed. Period.

Dr. Grossklaus then immediately broke his own edict by permitting the EU Representative, who (as William Faulkner once remarked of Ernest Hemingway) "has never been known to use a word that might send a reader to the dictionary," to liberally insert the word "food" in front of "supplements" throughout the Guidelines, even though no brackets were involved there. This move was initially astounding but became typical of the rest of the meeting as it became increasingly clear that this was really a Meeting of Two, the EU Representative and the Chairman. The rest of us were nothing more than road bumps on their screeching drag race to regulatory heaven.

Several delegations, including those of the United States and the NHF, objected to this first move. In particular, I told the Committee that if the EU were to be permitted to open up unbracketed text, then we and others deserved the same right. But the Chairman brushed these objections aside and quickly approved the EU Representative's insertions. We then sped on. Yet, this initial action set the tone as well as the rhythm for the rest of the meeting.

So, feeling a bit like Mel Gibson's soldiers in the film "We Were Soldiers Once and Young," dropped into enemy territory and surrounded on all sides, we began to take our share of hostile fire. But, then, we gave it back too.

The United States Is Outclassed and Outmaneuvered.

Treated as an almost-important delegation by the Gang of Two, the United States suffers from the fatal indignity of being North American and not European. In the wildly pro-European Codex Committee meetings, the United States does not stand a chance. Despite its large population, territory, economic and military might, and not even to mention the fact that it pays a larger per-capita share of the United Nations' budget (which includes the WHO and the FAO) than does the European Union, the Gang of Two has decided that in the language of "consensus," the European Unions' 17 member states at Codex count for more than the United States. And, by the interesting way, the EU at these meetings also counts for more than populous India or China. From what

I can see, Third-World countries are either bought out or shut out; and they do not speak up enough in defense of their true interests.

The Committee is supposed to reach "consensus" on each point before setting it in stone and moving on. According to the Codex Committee on General Principles, "consensus" is generally defined as the absence of sustained opposition. But, as he announced at this very meeting, the Chairman defines "consensus" as "everyone gets to be heard." Well, that's lovely. It is also very wrong. But this made-up definition is cleverly convenient for the EU, which helps explain how the EU always gets its way.

Whenever the EU Representative encounters a roadblock in getting his way, the Chairman will "helpfully" ask the Committee if perhaps the opposing sides could discuss this during a break and reach a compromise. This happened at least twice during this Agenda item, and both times the United States was outmaneuvered by the EU.

One example is typical: The United States delegate sought to delete a short, bracketed sentence from the vitamin-and-minerals definition of the Guidelines because it added nothing to the definition and was even confusing to readers. The US was supported in this move by South Africa, New Zealand, Zimbabwe, Brazil, Venezuela, Turkey, India, Cuba, the Council for Responsible Nutrition (CRN), and the NHF. But the EU Representative said no to the deletion, and was supported in turn by a few EU-member countries (who should not be counted twice), Switzerland, Australia, Thailand, and Malaysia. Even though the bulk of the delegates were clearly in favor of deleting the sentence and opposed the EU, the Chairman suggested that a compromise be worked out during the break that was then upon us.

During the break, the US and the EU supposedly compromised. The US would agree to leaving the sentence in the definitions paragraph in a modified form if the EU Representative would agree to the deletion of another sentence in a later paragraph (about Safe Upper Limits) that was more important to the US. The two sides agreed and the sentence, as modified, stayed in.

Yet, when the later paragraph arrived for discussion, and it was time for the EU Representative to deliver on his promise to delete the sentence that "[w]hen maximum levels are set, due account should be taken to the reference intake values of vitamins and min-

erals for the population," the EU Representative *opposed* the deletion. When I later rhetorically asked the United States delegate,
Dr. Barbara Schneeman, whether she had liked being stabbed in
the back, she tried to explain away the EU Representative's
changed position. This only showed me that she had not been prepared to stand up to the EU in the way necessary to prevent from
being run over roughshod.

I must say, though, that upon meeting Dr. Schneeman, I was
immediately struck with and impressed by her clear intelligence,
frankness, and refreshing willingness to actually listen to and consider others' viewpoints, including mine. She is also very articulate
and likeable. It is just unfortunate that Americans are such terrible
political negotiators. Americans make great businessmen and
women, great inventors, and even great soldiers; but put them in a
political conference room and they are almost always putty to be
molded by others. In this specific case, I suspect it may really be
because the American delegation actually shares the regulatory
mindset of the EU Representative and therefore has no philosophical grounding to oppose that view.

It would take many more pages than are available here to
provide examples from this Codex meeting supportive of my view.
However, the proof, as always, rests in the results of this meeting.
The Codex Guidelines are following the grim course laid out some
time ago by the European Union, not the more libertarian principles of health freedom found in the United States (and for which
the US delegation was probably not even instructed to fight).

The Guidelines Race On To Completion
Amidst Insults To Those Opposed.

As at last year's meeting, South Africa and the NHF were the
only vocal health-freedom proponents at this year's meeting. But,
like auditors at an Enron board meeting, we were not particularly
welcome.

Near the end of the first day, the Chairman must have tired of
hearing from the NHF because he refused to recognize me to speak
even though my request light was illuminated for some 45 minutes.
I had to go up to him at the end of the day and tell him that he was
ignoring me and that I would appreciate being recognized the
following day. To his credit, the NHF was recognized to speak at all

times the next day.

At another time, a couple of characters from the International Alliance of Dietary/Food Supplement Associations (IADSA) came up to the NHF's table to angrily complain that the NHF was "ruining everything" by opposing the Guidelines. They seemed quite unhappy, which confirmed to us that we were doing our job. IADSA is a fan of "reasonable" restrictions on consumer access to food supplements, which restrictions are actually not reasonable at all but truly harsh and anti-consumer. It is hard for me to believe that IADSA's member associations and companies would knowingly spend money to have IADSA as their representative at these meetings promoting these anti-supplement views while it runs up after-hours bar tabs with its EU Representative buddy.

Surprisingly, I, the life of the party, was not invited to join in these drinkfests. Instead, during the meeting, the EU Representative was snide and insulting towards me because of my strong and repeated opposition to his views. On my part, I was astounded to see the boldness with which the EU Representative actually gave verbal instructions (not suggestions), in front of all the delegations, to the Chairman as to what rulings he should make! And when he did not do that, on occasion, the Chairman asked him what to do!

So, by the middle of the second day, Tuesday, the Committee had completed its review of Agenda Item 4 despite the best efforts of the pro-freedom South African delegation and the NHF to make positive changes. The US seemed happy enough though, stating at one point that the United States "is supportive of the Chairman's efforts to move the text to closure." So much for following American law that forbids harmonization. And with that last whimper, the Guidelines are being shipped on to Rome, Italy for review and final approval by the Codex Alimentarius Commission next Summer.

The European Union's Game Plan

The EU's game plan is simple: Create a Fortress Europe. With the draconian EU's Food Supplements Directive (FSD) on the brink of throttling the internal food-supplements market throughout the European Union by limiting both types and potencies of supplements, the EU wants to get the same restrictions in place internationally through the Codex process. Once the international restrictions are in place, then those nasty, high-potency American supplements with those strange-sounding names cannot ever possibly be lawfully imported into the European Union. That is why the EU Representative is so insistent upon getting the exact same wording adopted in the Codex Guidelines as is found in the EU FSD.

Now, with the recent committee adoption of the Codex Guidelines for Food Supplements, the EU has successfully created a framework and structure into which it will later drop in restrictive "Safe" Upper Limits and restrictive Positive Lists of vitamins and minerals, just as they are having in the European Union. With Europe locked down tight, nothing possibly competitive with the pharmaceutical industry can threaten its European market.

The so-called "science-based risk assessment" for establishing Safe Upper Limits (maximum levels) for vitamin-and-mineral potencies, to which the EU has agreed, and about which the Americans are as happy as flies on cow dung, is nothing but a trap. The Americans think that they will be able to get real science to establish high maximum levels for their vitamins and minerals and then sell them to European consumers by the bushels. But by the time the Europeans get through applying their science, those maximum limits will be so low toddlers would be lucky to get any nutritional value out of Codex-harmonized vitamins and minerals. The European Union's Scientific Committee on Food has already started using its science-based risk assessment to establish laughably low maximum limits for European vitamins. And, lately, I have begun to see a growing concern, if not outright fear, in the faces of some science-based risk-assessment proponents that perhaps things might not go their way here after all.

Are the Guidelines Optional or Mandatory?

But the real question, for non-Europeans at least, is not whether the European Union will commit nutritional suicide; but rather whether the Europeans will take the rest of the world down with them by exporting their insane, anti-supplement paranoia to other shores. Strong arguments have been made that "it cannot happen in America," that domestic laws are safe-guarded from international interference both by treaty and by internal legislation.

Suzan Walter, the president of the American Holistic Health Association and a press attendee who has covered several Codex meetings, has observed that the Codex Guidelines, in ¶1.2, ominously state that "These Guidelines **do apply** in those jurisdictions where products defined in 2.1 [i.e., vitamin and mineral food supplements] are regulated as foods." (emphasis added). Moreover, the World Trade Organization (WTO), which will determine how a Codex text will be applied as to member countries, will look to the content of the text to see if it is mandatory or optional.

Given the mandatory language in ¶1.2, both the South African and Tanzanian delegations as well as the NHF asked the Chairman to specify whether these Guidelines were optional or mandatory. The Chairman deferred to the Codex Secretariat who firmly told us all that the Guidelines were optional. Yet, in an alarming move, when these delegations tried to have the clarifying language inserted into the Guidelines, both the EU and the US objected, saying it was unnecessary; and the language was rejected. South Africa then asked that its request for the language at least be noted in the final Report of the Meeting.

That, however, was not even allowed. Upon the Committee's reading of the draft Report of the Meeting, on the last day, I noticed that there was absolutely no mention of South Africa's request. When I asked the Chairman to insert language saying that South Africa and the NHF had asked whether the Guidelines were optional or mandatory and the Codex Secretariat had responded that they were optional, the Chairman refused! His refusal not only violated the Codex Alimentarius Commission's own Procedural Manual, but revealed the true nature of these Guidelines. It was also typical of his other refusals, too numerous to mention here, to allow the Report to be corrected or supplemented. As a result, the Report is inaccurate, untruthful, and cannot be trusted.

Another observer, who has covered many Codex meetings, has expressed her opinion that every WTO member country has signed mutual recognition agreements that *require* them to engage in a constant process of harmonization. As such, the United States and other countries will eventually be forced to harmonize to the Codex "guidelines." Thus, the question of whether the Guidelines are optional or not may be long-since answered.

Which Way Now?

The Guidelines for Vitamin and Mineral Food Supplements will be discussed and argued at the Codex Alimentarius Commission in Rome this coming Summer. At that time, the Commission can either accept or reject the just-approved draft Food Supplement Guidelines, either in whole or in part. The Commission could then send them back to the Bonn Committee for re-review and discussion. Rome will thus be an important battleground for this matter and the NHF will be there.

Regardless, the Guidelines as they presently exist are nothing more than a very open framework. For them to have any real meaning, certain key components, such as the establishment of Safe Upper Limits, must be created and agreed upon. This will take time and political capital to accomplish. As the developing countries awaken to the realization that they, as much as the Americans, are being excluded from European markets, there is a good chance that they will organize and fight back to prevent these final components from being fitted into the framework just created. We can already see this resistance developing.

As I have always believed, the restrictive, anti-consumer Codex standards sought by the European Union, even if put in place, will never endure. The marketplace, as it always does, will reassert itself and reasonable, healthy international standards will emerge. In fact, I predict that in 30-50 years, social historians will be holding up the current anti-supplement regulators as yet another example of silly, delusional thinking on par with those who once believed the earth was flat or that man would never fly. They will be uniformly laughed at and ridiculed. Our job, though, is just to prevent them from harming people in the meantime.

The future is known, it is the past that keeps changing.
- *Unknown Soviet Union dissident*

South Africa Opposes Codex Rule on Food Health Information

By Sepp Hasslberger

(June 2004)

The international food standard setting body, Codex Alimentarius has been deliberating a guideline to determine what information food product labels may contain. The draft guideline, which is ready to be adopted at the next meeting of the Codex Alimentarius Commission in Geneva, Switzerland, to be held from 28 June to 3 July 2004, says that **no information may be given regarding any food's effects for the prevention, alleviation or cure of any disease.**

South Africa has asked to change the wording of the guideline, as clearly scientific evidence shows that foods do have disease preventive and even curative properties. Governments the world over recommend that we eat at least five servings of fruit and vegetables a day, to prevent cancer and other diseases. Scurvy, which killed many sailors, could only be prevented when skippers realized that citrus fruits contained some element that was vital for health.

The Food and Agricultural Organization, which is the "parent organization" of Codex, has published a report[1] on food and the prevention of chronic diseases, while a team of scientists at Johns Hopkins in Baltimore, in collaboration with the WHO, found in recent research that nutrition could save the lives of millions of kids every year. It was estimated that feeding all children world-wide an adequate diet would prevent about 1 million deaths a year from pneumonia, 800,000 from diarrhea, 500,000 from malaria, and 250,000 from measles.

The question is: why, if eating certain foods is important for the prevention of disease, are we not allowed to know? Is big pharma consolidating a monopoly for anything to do with disease?

See the arguments of the South African Codex delegation regarding disease prevention claims (information to consumers) for food:

"Comments from South Africa to the Codex Commission (2004) CL 2004/22-FL Draft Guideline for Use of Nutrition and Health Claims at Step 8 for adoption by the Commission

South Africa is concerned that a Draft Guideline is presented for adoption at Step 8 that contains a section that is no longer sustainable because of overwhelming scientific evidence that contradicts the message of this section. Since Codex adopted the principle that Standards and Guidelines should be based on scientific evidence, the above-mentioned Guideline should not be adopted at Step 8 with this section still in operation.

In the following documents, the WHO, acknowledges the role of **"diet and nutrition in the prevention of chronic diseases",** and the **"promotion of optimal nutrition among consumers through adequate Labeling and the use of health claims, to assist them in making the right choices":**

1. "WHO Technical Report on Diet, Nutrition and the Prevention of Chronic Diseases" (2003)
2. WHO's Director-General's report of the Joint FAO/WHO evaluations of the work of the Codex Alimentarius Commission (Fifty-sixth World Health Assembly Provisional agenda 14.19, reference A 56/34, dated 3 April 2004), paragraph 23. In paragraph 17 the Director-General noted that the

Codex Commission recommends that the scope of the Commission should also fully cover health-related aspects of food standards.

In our opinion two Codex Committee's failed to implement this policy recommendation of science-based decisions, namely CCNFSDU 2003 and CCFL 2004 by not acknowledging -

1. In the case of CCNFSDU 2003: The use of the wording **"prevention of chronic diseases"** in the preamble to the document Proposed Draft Guidelines for Vitamin and Mineral supplements", based on an outdated clause in the Codex general Guidelines on Claims (CAC/GL 1-1979 (Rev. 1-1991) which prohibits claims as to the suitability of a food for use in the prevention, alleviation, treatment or cure of a disease; and

2. In the case of CCFL 2004: The revision of the Codex general Guidelines on Claims (CAC/GL 1-1979 (Rev. 1-1991) to update the abovementioned clause to reflect the latest scientific evidence that nutrients can heal nutritional deficiency diseases and certain metabolic disorders, can prevent chronic diseases and can be used as an alternative option in the treatment of some diseases.

WHO finds it acceptable to use the word "diseases" when referring to diet and nutritional policies which are within the scope of Codex Alimentarius. In other words, the fact that foods and nutrients can prevent diseases and in some cases cure diseases (e.g., classical deficiency diseases and certain metabolic disorders) do not make these foods and nutrients medicines from a scientific point of view.

Dictations from national legislation should not be permitted to influence and allow incorrect statements in a global Guideline.

South Africa recommends that the Draft Guideline for Use of Nutrition and Health Claims not be adopted at step 8 by the Commission and that section 3.4 of the Codex General Guidelines on Claims (CAC/GL 1-1979 (Rev. 1-1991) which prohibits claims as to the suitability of a food for use in the prevention, alleviation, treatment or cure of a disease be revised to correctly reflect scientific evidence."

---

[1](http:/www.amazon.com/exec/obidos/ASIN/924120916X/masternewmedi/102-2027811-1086568?dev-t=D291Y9X6FSA21J&camp=2025&link_code=xm2).

Codex - The Root of the Problem Identified

by Paul Anthony Taylor

(Published in *Health Freedom News*, Vol. 22, No. 3, Summer 2004)

As a reader of *Health Freedom News* you will no doubt by now be very familiar with the threat that Codex poses to the future global availability of high-dose dietary supplements. At the November 2003 meeting of the Codex Committee on Nutrition and Foods for Special Dietary Uses (CCNFSDU) for example, the Codex Guidelines on Vitamin and Mineral Supplements advanced from step 3 to step 5 of the 8-stage Codex ratification process. As such, the danger is growing that an unjustifiably restrictive Codex standard for vitamins and minerals could now be finalized within the next twelve months. The danger that this poses to our future health and freedoms does not need to be spelled out.

Nevertheless, what is not often appreciated is that the CCNFSDU is only one of around 20 different Codex committees that are currently engaged in the act of setting global "standards" for our food supply under the guise of free trade "harmonization."

Another one of these committees for example, is the Codex Committee on Food Labeling (CCFL), whose mandate is to draft provisions for what can and cannot be said on the labels of food products, including of course those on dietary supplements. This committee meets annually in Canada, and at its most recent meeting, in May of this year, it agreed to advance a text on Guidelines for the Use of Nutrition and Health Claims to step 8 of the Codex process. Following a subsequent meeting of the Codex Alimentarius Commission that was held in Geneva from 28th June to 3rd July of this year the Nutrition and Health Claims text was then ratified as a finalized Codex standard.

The Codex General Guidelines on Claims

Upon first examining the text of the Codex Guidelines for the Use of Nutrition and Health Claims one might be forgiven for thinking that it would allow a wide variety of health claims for dietary supplements, as amongst other things it states that health claims should be permitted provided that they are based on current relevant scientific substantiation. Hidden away amongst the preamble to the text however is the following somewhat innocuous-looking statement: "*Claims of the type described in Section 3.4 of the Codex General Guidelines on Claims are prohibited.*"

What then, one might reasonably wonder, are the claims described in Section 3.4 of the Codex General Guidelines on Claims? Following a little digging around on the Codex website to find the relevant document one unearths a MAJOR problem however, in that it turns out that section 3.4 of the Codex General Guidelines on Claims states the following:

"*3. PROHIBITED CLAIMS*

3.4 Claims as to the suitability of a food for use in the prevention, alleviation, treatment or cure of a disease, disorder, or particular physiological condition unless they are:

(a) in accordance with the provisions of Codex standards or guidelines for foods under jurisdiction of the Committee on Foods for Special Dietary Uses and follow the principles set forth in these guidelines; . . . ."

As such therefore, given that dietary supplements are treated as foods by Codex, a global standard has now been set that would, when enforced, prohibit the labels of dietary supplements from carrying statements that the product can prevent, alleviate, treat or cure ANY disease or health condition.

In theory of course, exemption (a) allows the CCNFSDU to make a provision for health claims for dietary supplements if it wished. In practice however this is extremely unlikely to happen. At last year's meeting, for example, the head of the EU delegation said that "food and the prevention of diseases do not go together," and that "health claims for vitamin and mineral supplements should be prohibited." Similarly, the chairman of the CCNFSDU said that "drugs are to mitigate and prevent diseases," and that "the role of food supplements is to support the diet." These views, in fact, are currently shared by the vast majority of the national delegations at Codex. As such we can be quite certain that health claims of the type described under Section 3.4 of the Codex General Guidelines on Claims will be prohibited.

As a result therefore, the setting of this new global standard for Nutrition and Health Claims now raises some fundamental questions.

The FDA Fails to Defend U.S. Law at Codex.

The head of the U.S. delegation at the Montreal Codex meeting was a Mr. L. Robert Lake, who is currently Director of the Office of Regulations and Policy at the Center for Food Safety and Applied Nutrition in the FDA. Why then, one wonders, didn't Mr. Lake object to the prohibition on health claims for food products when he knew that by agreeing to it he was supporting something that could deny US consumers access to truthful health information? In the case of Pearson v. Shalala, for example, the decision of the United States Court of Appeals for the DC Circuit Court reaffirmed consumers' First Amendment right to learn about dietary supplements without unnecessary interference from the FDA. Nevertheless, Mr. Lake seemingly believes that he and the FDA have the right to ignore both this judgment and the free-speech amendment of the US Constitution when participating in the setting of global standards at Codex meetings.

In contrast, however, the delegation of South Africa (who, other than NHF, are currently the only consistently pro-health freedom delegation at Codex) specifically stated at the Montreal meeting that section 3.4 was "no longer sustainable or morally justifiable," and in a passionate speech, Mrs. Antoinette Booyzen, the head of the South African delegation, argued that:

"In allowing this clause to remain in this Codex Guideline, this committee evades its responsibility to people of this planet, by censoring evidence-based scientific information of the role of nutrition in prevention,

alleviation, treatment and cure of disease."

Mrs. Booyzen then went on to say that:

"The question this committee must consider today is: Are we fully pre-pared to acknowledge the role of optimum nutrition in the prevention, alleviation, treatment and cure of disease, and thereby acknowledge the Codex principle of basing its standards and guidelines on science?"

Nevertheless, her proposal received no support at all from the other national delegations, who one by one spoke up to oppose it. Mr. L. Robert Lake for example, when it came to his turn to speak, on behalf of the US delegation, simply stated that: "We want to join with the other delegations that oppose work on this item."

Who Benefits from the Prohibition on Health Claims?

The real question that we should now therefore be asking ourselves is: Who really benefits from the censoring of evidence-based scientific information on the role of nutrition in the prevention, alleviation, treatment, and cure of disease?

Consumers? Most definitely not. Manufacturers of dietary supplements? No way.

The pharmaceutical industry? Of course, as the prohibition ensures that the only products that can make claims relating to the prevention, alleviation, treatment, and cure of disease are pharmaceutical drugs.

And does the FDA benefit from this censorship? Naturally, as it receives vast sums of money from pharmaceutical companies in return for issuing drug licenses.

What about the Federal Government? They too benefit from the prohibition, as they in turn receive vast amounts of income in the form of taxes on pharmaceutical company profits.

As a result we have now gotten down to the very root of the problem: **By prohibiting all claims that food can prevent, allevi-ate, treat, or cure disease, Section 3.4 of the Codex General Guidelines on Claims essentially protects the patent on the phar-maceutical industry's control of our healthcare systems.**

Without this clause there would be nothing to prevent vitamin

PREAMBLE
TO THE CONSTITUTION OF FAO

THE NATIONS ACCEPTING THIS CONSTITUTION, BEING DETERMINED TO PROMOTE THE COMMON WELFARE BY FURTHERING SEPARATE AND COLLECTIVE ACTION ON THEIR PART FOR THE PURPOSES OF :

RAISING LEVELS OF NUTRITION AND STANDARDS OF LIVING OF THE PEOPLES UNDER THEIR RESPECTIVE JURISDICTIONS,

SECURING IMPROVEMENTS IN THE EFFICIENCY OF THE PRODUCTION AND DISTRIBUTION OF ALL FOOD AND AGRICULTURAL PRODUCTS,

BETTERING THE CONDITION OF RURAL POPULATIONS,

AND THUS CONTRIBUTING TOWARD AN EXPANDING WORLD ECONOMY,

HEREBY ESTABLISH THE FOOD AND AGRICULTURE ORGANIZATION OF THE UNITED NATIONS THROUGH WHICH THE MEMBERS WILL REPORT TO ONE ANOTHER ON THE MEASURES TAKEN AND THE PROGRESS ACHIEVED IN THE FIELDS OF ACTION SET FORTH ABOVE.

ON THE OCCASION OF THE 20 TH ANNIVERSARY, THE PREAMBLE OF THE CONSTITUTION WAS FORMALLY AMENDED TO RECOGNIZE THAT THE ULTIMATE OBJECTIVE OF ALL THE VARIOUS ACTIVITIES OF THE ORGANIZATION IS TO ENSURE FREEDOM FROM HUNGER FOR ALL MANKIND.

THE AMENDED CLAUSE NOW READS:

"AND THUS CONTRIBUTING TOWARD AN EXPANDING WORLD ECONOMY AND ENSURING HUMANITY'S FREEDOM FROM HUNGER"

Plaque of FAO Preamble mounted on wall at FAO's Headquarters in Rome, Italy (photograph by Scott Tips)

Pro-health-freedom South African delegate Antoinette Booyzen at CCNFSDU meeting in Bonn, Germany, November 2004.

NHF delegates Sepp Hasslberger, Scott Tips (delegation head), and Paul Anthony Taylor at CCNFSDU meeting in Bonn, Germany, November 2004

Photos of November 2005 CCNFSDU Meeting in Bonn, Germany.
Dr. Rob Verkerk, Scott Tips, Paul Anthony Taylor.

A delegate's eye view of the CCNFS-
DU meeting at the Brückenforum in
Bonn, Germany

Scott Tips presents NHF's 2004 Health Freedom
Hero Award to Mrs. Antoinette Booyzen in
Bonn, Germany

FAO Headquarters building in Rome, Italy,July 2005

Codex Alimentarius Commission meeting in Rome, Italy, July 2005

manufacturers from making the same type of claims for dietary supplements as the pharmaceutical industry does for its pharmaceutical drugs. Moreover, if this Section were dropped from the Codex General Guidelines on Claims, then *real* progress could at long last be made in building and cementing health freedom on a global scale.

The health-freedom movement must now therefore unite against the growing global restrictions that Codex is throwing in its way. In particular we must all now call on our national governments to support the dropping of Section 3.4 from the Codex General Guidelines on Claims.

There is no comparable industry on the planet where the manufacturers of a product are legally prevented from telling their customers the true facts about their products, especially when those facts are supported by many thousands of scientific studies. Therefore, unless and until Section 3.4 of the Codex General Guidelines on Claims is altered in such a way as it permits claims that food can prevent, alleviate, treat, or cure disease, the true properties of dietary supplements will always be censored by the regulators. If Section 3.4 were dropped, however, then dietary supplement manufacturers would gain the same rights in advertising their products as are currently enjoyed by their pharmaceutical cousins.

Once one understands this, it can easily be seen that the FDA, the Federal Government, and governments across the globe will oppose the scrapping of Section 3.4 every step of the way, because doing so would in time dramatically reduce the income that they receive from the issuing of drug licenses and taxes on pharmaceutical company profits. But in the name of progress, and for the future of healthcare on planet earth, scrap it we must.

Where are Our Taxes Going?

An elderly uncle of mine in the UK was recently telling me how he had been unable to get a doctor to come out to see his wife when she had suffered a mini-stroke one evening. Thirty years ago, he reminded me, it would have been possible to get a doctor to come out right away. Clearly then, despite the fact that within a couple of years the UK government will be spending around £100 billion annually on its National Health Service (NHS), the *quality* of healthcare that UK citizens receive is decreasing year by year.

Why is this so? Quite simply because along with the rest of the Western world, the UK NHS is being crippled by the cost of paying for outrageously expensive pharmaceutical drugs. The fact that much of this money is being spent on unnecessary, ineffective, and even harmful treatments – when safer and more effective natural therapies are already known to exist borders upon insanity. As such, the scrapping of Section 3.4 of the Codex General Guidelines on Claims would also free up billions of dollars of taxpayers' money and circumvent the bankrupting of our healthcare systems. And this is before we even begin to consider the further savings that would ensue from increased numbers of consumers actively engaging in preventative healthcare via the consumption of dietary supplements.

Risk-Analysis, or Risk-Benefit Analysis?

There is yet another aspect to all of this however. Section 3.4 is also the reason why our regulators engage in risk-analysis assessment of dietary supplements instead of in risk-**benefit** analysis, as under this clause the benefits of dietary supplements -other than the prevention of simple deficiencies are not supposed to exist. Once Section 3.4 was removed from the Codex General Guidelines on Claims, however, there would be no reason not to engage in proper benefit-analysis; and the well-documented beneficial properties of dietary supplements would finally be out in the open for all to see.

From this point onwards therefore we must all be absolutely certain where we stand. If we want to defend our access to dietary supplements and achieve real health freedom we cannot stand idly by and hope that others will do it for us.

The scrapping of Section 3.4 of the Codex General Guidelines on Claims would be a major step in the right direction, and it is up to us **all** to demand that it comes about. Please therefore write to your senators and congressmen, as our future access to truthful health information now depends in no small part upon this next big step.

Codex Guidelines for Vitamin and Mineral Supplements: The Controversy Continues

By Paul Anthony Taylor

November 2004

November 2004 – During the first week of November the so-called "Codex Committee on Nutrition and Foods for Special Dietary Uses" (CCNFSDU) met again in Bonn, Germany to discuss their controversial Guidelines for Vitamin and Mineral Supplements. As widely predicted the Committee agreed to complete their deliberations on this occasion and to advance the Guidelines for adoption at Step 8, which is effectively the final stage in the process. As a result of this decision the Guidelines will now be considered at a meeting of the Codex Alimentarius Commission, due to take place in Rome in July 2005, in order for the text to be ratified and adopted as a newly agreed global standard.

The History of the Guidelines

The Guidelines for Vitamin and Mineral Supplements have been under discussion at Codex since the 1990s, and were originally intended to limit the maximum amounts of all vitamins and minerals contained in supplements to RDA levels only. This proposal, predictably, had caused widespread outrage amongst consumers when it first emerged. At its meeting in November 2003 however, following persistently vehement opposition from Dr. Rath and the global health-freedom movement, the CCNFSDU finally gave in and decreed that the maximum levels would instead be determined by scientific risk assessment. Ominously, however, and in a sign of things to come, the Guidelines were also advanced from Step 3 to Step 5 of the 8-step Codex approval process at this same meeting.

Following a subsequent meeting of the Codex Alimentarius Commission that took place in Geneva from 28th June to 3rd July 2004, the Guidelines were then further advanced to Step 7 of the process – only a hair's breadth from completion. It was with this background in mind therefore that 280 delegates, observers, and advisors representing 62 Member countries and 25 International Non-Governmental Organizations assembled at the Bruckenforum in Bonn for this year's meeting.

The Influence of the EU and the Bias of the Chairman

The discussions that took place at this years meeting in Bonn essentially followed the same pattern as those of last year, in that the Chairman of the Committee, Dr. Rolf Grossklaus, once again appeared to show a clear preference and bias towards the demands of the delegate from the EU Commission, Mr. Basil Mathioudakis. Whenever there was disagreement amongst the Committee over any aspect of the text, for example, Dr. Grossklaus unfailingly came down clearly and unequivocally on the side of Mr. Mathioudakis and the EU. As a result some parts of the Codex Guidelines for Vitamin and Mineral Supplements now bear a very strong resemblance to sections of the equally controversial EU Food Supplements Directive.

Inaccuracies in the Official Codex Meeting Report

The official reports that are released following Codex meetings are not always strictly accurate, and frequently do not reflect either the discussions that took place or the manner in which things were "decided." Unsurprisingly, therefore, there are several instances in this years CCNFSDU report of events being rewritten to give the illusion of democracy during the meeting.

For example, the report states that the Committee decided to focus its discussions on those sections of the Guidelines for Vitamin and Mineral Supplements that were contained in square brackets. However, because the sections in square brackets were merely those few sentences that could not be agreed by the Committee at their previous meeting this decision was a particularly crucial one, as it had the effect of severely limiting the scope of the discussions that took place. In reality, though, and what the report did not say, was that at the start of the meeting the Chairman, Dr. Grossklaus, had actually instructed the Committee that the discussion should focus on those parts of the text that were still in square brackets. As a result therefore the Committee was not allowed any choice in the matter, and whenever anybody tried to open up discussion on controversial areas of the text that were not in square brackets Dr. Grossklaus simply prevented them from doing so.

Similarly, the report also states that the Committee, "recognizing that considerable progress had been made on the text, agreed to advance the Draft Guidelines for adoption at Step 8 by the 28th Session of the Codex Alimentarius Commission." In fact, however, what actually occurred was that Dr. Grossklaus said that he wanted to advance the Guidelines for adoption at Step 8, and the Committee were once again not given an opportunity to discuss the matter.

Worse still however, some important discussions that took place during the meeting are not even mentioned in the report. The National Health Federation (NHF), for example, who are the only consistently pro-health freedom non-governmental organization attending Codex, had specifically requested during the meeting that it should be stated either in the text of the Guidelines or in the report itself whether or not it was mandatory for countries to implement the Guidelines. Dr. Jeronimas Maskeliunas answered the NHF's question on behalf of the Codex Secretariat, and stated that all documents that the Committee is elaborating are "not mandatory." He also stated that "member countries decide how to use them." The NHF therefore requested that this should be stated in the report.

When the draft report was distributed on the final day of the meeting, however, there was no mention to be found in it of either the NHF's question or Dr. Maskeliunas' answer. The NHF therefore raised this with the Chairman, and made repeated requests to him to include mention of this important issue in the official report to be released following the meeting. Nevertheless, Dr. Grossklaus refused to allow this, saying that it was not mandatory for him to heed such requests. As far as the report is concerned therefore, it is as if this vital matter had not even been discussed.

The Concept of a "Framework" Document

The Guidelines that were passed in Bonn will not immediately ban natural therapies and Cellular Medicine however. Because of the tremendous opposition to these Guidelines the text that was agreed in Bonn this year is only a "framework" document, and will not set any of the more controversial aspects of the Guideline that the Codex Alimentarius Commission would originally like to have had included. For example, the maximum levels to be permitted in vitamin and mineral supplements will now be set separately at a later, currently unspecified, date. Similarly, and unlike the EU Food Supplements Directive, the Guideline does not contain a list of permitted nutrient sources (the so-called "positive list") and nor was any language added to the text this year to allow for the later addition of such a list.

As such, the Codex Alimentarius Commission is clearly hoping that consumers will be lulled into a false sense of security when they learn that the completed Guidelines for Vitamin and Mineral Supplements will not immediately ban natural therapies and Cellular Medicine. Nevertheless, it is now clear that the overall plan is to add the most controversial aspects of the vitamin-and-mineral restrictions one step at a time, in the hope that if the Codex Alimentarius Commission proceeds slowly enough consumers will not be roused into any significant forms of opposition until it is too late.

FAO/WHO Nutrient Risk-Assessment Project

On the subject of the risk analysis process that will be used to set the maximum levels, it is interesting to note that the World Health Organization (WHO) representative stated during the Codex meeting that the WHO was in favor of moving from a non-nutrient approach to a nutrient-appropriate approach. On the face of it this is good news, because as we know nutrients are not poisons and they are absolutely essential for life. Nevertheless we should not be fooled by this rhetoric, and nor should we be lulled into any false sense of security over it.

In September 2004, for example, the Food and Agriculture Organization of the United Nations (FAO) and the WHO announced a joint nutrient risk-assessment project intended to define a "scientifically-based" and "internationally applicable" approach for nutrient risk assessment. The aim of the project is described as being to provide scientific advice on the principles and methodologies to be used in conducting risk assessments for nutrients and related substances.

However, because the FAO and the WHO are the joint administrators of the Codex Alimentarius Commission the results of their nutrient risk-assessment project will be hugely influential upon the maximum levels to be recommended by Codex in connection with the Guidelines for Vitamin and Mineral Food Supplements. Worryingly, therefore, the background paper published by the FAO/WHO when the project was announced tends to suggest that the published Opinions of the EU Scientific Committee on Food (SCF) will be very influential upon the outcome of the FAO/WHO risk-assessment work. This does nothing to inspire confidence in the FAO/WHO nutrient risk-assessment project, as many of the SCF's published Opinions run completely contrary to not only the principles of Cellular Medicine but also to common sense itself. The SCF's opinion on Vitamin B3 for example suggests that the Upper Safe Level of niacin should be set at only 10mg, an amount that is just over half of the EU RDA.

Clearly, therefore, we must view the FAO/WHO nutrient risk assessment project with a healthy dose of skepticism.

More Delegations Supporting South Africa

On a brighter note however, South Africa, who in recent years has been the only consistently pro-health freedom national delegation attending Codex, received a great deal of support at this years meeting not just from the NHF but also from the national delegations of India, Tanzania. Ghana, and Zimbabwe. This was an important breakthrough because although the number of pro-health freedom delegations attending Codex meetings remains small, it is at least finally beginning to grow. As such, whilst there still remains much work to be done in this area in order to convince further countries to argue in favor of health freedom at Codex, it is now becoming increasingly clear that in this respect the tide is very slowly beginning to turn in our favor.

South Africa Retained Chairmanship of NRVs Working Group

Another positive outcome from this year's Codex meeting was that South Africa managed to retain the Chairmanship of the working group that will be setting the new nutrient reference values (NRVs). The South African delegation has consistently drawn attention to the fact that the traditional RDA approach to nutrition does not promote optimum health, and they will now be arguing for the NRVs to be set at levels which take into account the prevention and reduction of diseases and the maintenance of an optimum nutritional status.

The working group will now therefore be continuing its work, and amongst other things will be establishing the scientific basis upon which the NRVs will be set, the range of nutrients to be included and the criteria for their selection.

Conclusion

Although the text of the Codex Guidelines for Vitamin and Mineral Supplements has now been completed, its most important aspects have still to be determined.

Moreover, whilst the Codex Alimentarius Commission is obviously keen to promote the idea that the maximum levels will be set scientifically, there are now very good grounds to believe that the process involved in doing so will be subject to undue influence from the EU and the pharmaceutical-medical orthodoxy, who will doubtlessly be doing everything that they can to ensure that the maximum levels are set as low as possible.

We already know from the text of the Guidelines, for example, that the maximum levels will be set by taking into account the daily intake from other dietary sources. In other words, when setting the maximum levels it is likely that the nutrient intake from food will be deducted from the levels that are set by the scientific risk-assessment process. It is not difficult to predict therefore that the nutrient levels that we are supposedly getting from our food will be calculated to be as high as possible, despite the fact that scientific research has repeatedly shown that the mineral content of our fruits and vegetables has been falling worldwide for over half a century.

Similarly the text of the Guidelines also states that when setting the maximum levels account should also be taken of the reference intake values of vitamins and minerals for the population. This therefore raises the worrying possibility that regulators will be able to use the low levels that have been established in population reference values to still further reduce the maximum levels in their own individual countries.

Clearly therefore the controversy surrounding the Codex Guidelines for Vitamin and Mineral Supplements seems set to continue for some time to come. Whilst some groups are already falsely claiming that consumers will benefit from the finalization of the Codex Guidelines for Vitamin and Mineral Supplements, it is now increasingly clear that such claims are not based upon the true facts. We must all now therefore remain vigilant, and each and every one of us must do everything that we can to protect the future of Cellular Medicine and natural therapies both for ourselves and for future generations.

He alone is great and happy who requires neither to command nor to obey in order to secure his being of some importance in the world.

- Johann Wolfgang von Goethe

Codex Nutrition Committee: Supplement Guidelines Final

By Sepp Hasslberger

(Posted November 3, 2004)

Tuesday, 2 November 2004 – The Codex Alimentarius Nutrition Committee sitting in a week-long conclave here in Bonn, formerly the capital of Germany, has concluded its deliberations of proposed international *Guidelines for Vitamin and Mineral Supplements*. I am sitting in this meeting together with Scott Tips and Paul Taylor of the National Health Federation [http://www.thenhf.com], one of the only consumer-centered bodies allowed in the meetings, and certainly the only NGO that has a strong pro-choice stand and is actually allowed a voice of comment, if not vote.

The delegates from around the World ironed out remaining differences and agreed to call the proposal a finished product, to be referred to the *Codex Alimentarius Commission*, the executive body which has to give its final approval, probably by early July 2005. This decision ends a tedious decade-long marathon of what at times looked like a tug of war between countries supporting wide use of supplements for health and others much more cautious over the implications of having to import expensive nutrient-rich products, while their populations do not even have sufficient, let alone nutritious, foods.

Industry representatives are satisfied with the results. "We did not get all we wanted, but we can work with these guidelines" was one comment heard in the corridors of the meeting's forum from a U.S. industry representative who attended. Instead of severe dosage limitations – the original idea was to apply the minimal Recommended Daily Amounts or RDAs – it was agreed in last year's meeting to base possible dosage limitations on scientific risk analysis.

Nutrients are quite different from toxic chemicals, the first substances evaluated in this way. But work is underway to adapt the risk analysis principles to nutrients, which are vital parts of the diet, rather than contaminants. This is a separate project under the Codex Nutrition Committee, a year-round work group chaired by the Australian delegation, which will continue work in this coming year. In addition, FAO has announced that it will do its own work on risk assessment, which is part of the overall discipline of risk analysis.

There is also a work group charged with looking at *nutrient reference* values, which are the RDA amounts we find as percentages on food labels, such as – "this product contains 150 % of the recommended daily amount of Vitamin K."

Consumers do look at such indications and if supplements are to promote optimal health, the figures must be right. There is a great opportunity here for those who believe nutritional products are the solution to our current health crisis. The science of nutritional intervention for health now has a chance to enter the mainstream and leave its mark on the official health advice provided to consumers.

The supplement *Guidelines*, as agreed by the Committee, provide – at least for now – merely a statement of general principles. They do not mandate anything specific about either the sources of vitamins and minerals that can be used in the formulation of such products, nor do they restrict dosages, other than saying that future limits must be based on an analysis of the risks yet to be performed.

It appears that, apart from protesting against potentially restrictive Codex Guidelines for supplements, opposition may have to shift gears and bring the fight to the scientific arena. Energies might be well spent in providing scientific documentation attesting to the extremely low risk inherent in supplement use as well as to the efficacy of nutrients in prevention and health.

Standards or Guidelines?

Codex Alimentarius is in the business of crafting international standards, guidelines, and related documents to facilitate cross-border trade in foods and protect the health of consumers. Countries may decide whether to apply such rules or not. Traditionally, *guidelines* were thought to be less binding than food *standards*, but independent research shows that this distinction has become eroded over time. The difference may now be more semantic than real.

In 1995, Codex Alimentarius and the then newly formed *World Trade Organization* agreed that WTO would use the documents elaborated by Codex as reference texts in the resolution of trade disputes. So while formerly, implementation of Codex documents was voluntary, this is no longer the case. As Suzan Walter of the American Holistic Health Association points out in comments published on the AHHA website, *"all texts provided by Codex to WTO, no matter what they are labeled, can be used as mandatory international trade regulations to be applied to every nation."* An open letter distributed to delegates before this year's Codex meeting gives a good overview of the enforcement issue.

There seems to be little awareness of this changed situation as yet. Some countries have expressly reserved their right to not apply the future *Guidelines on Supplements* because they classify those products as medicines – but there might be a snag. Regulating supplements under medicines law may not exempt Canada, Australia, Mexico, and some other Latin American nations from an eventual challenge to their laws under international trade agreements. Even for the United States, where politicians openly state that they do not intend to follow externally imposed regulations, a future trade dispute might bring an unexpected moment of truth.

The World Trade Organization appears set to make no distinction, but until there is an actual case, no one knows for sure – a real quandary because international law now seems to flow out of the relatively anonymous deliberations of health officials attending Codex meetings. For the most part, those officials have no national mandate that could bind their country, nor do they seem to be aware that their decisions may change national laws by-passing any parliamentary checks and balances. Under the WTO, trade sanctions are the tool to force compliance.

Some More History

Work on these Supplement Guidelines was first proposed by the

German delegation to the Codex Nutrition Committee in 1990. For several years, work progressed slowly but the agenda was kept alive by the Germans. At the time this was widely looked upon as a somewhat strange attempt to regulate supplements, coming as it did from a country that practically has no history of use of these products.

At the same time, Germany also introduced the idea of a *European Food Supplements Directive*. That effort was shelved for some years, after a first round of consultations showed that the field was much too difficult and contentious to regulate by directive. A few years later however – after Codex work on supplements had progressed – work re-started on the Food Supplements Directive. This renewed effort was largely driven by the UK and Germany and as it happened, the European directive made it to the finishing line two years before the Codex guidelines.

The European Food Supplements Directive may seem restrictive – indeed it has been challenged before the European Court of Justice over its prohibition of products that do not meet strict formulation criteria.

In shaping the Codex "consensus" on supplements, it appears that the EU directive provided a blueprint, a fact that was perhaps not given sufficient importance by non-European delegations. In the numerous meetings that led to the current text, corners were cut and at times, the German chairman Rolf Grossklaus and the representative of the European Union, Basil Mathioudakis, have been more or less openly accused of bending the rules.

Working in concert, the Germany/EU team seems to have acted to blunt initiatives of the developing countries as well as the English-speaking world, even excluding views of some delegations not strictly in agreement with what now appears to have been a pre-set agenda. The result – a text for the Codex Supplements Guidelines that reads remarkably similar to the European Food Directive. Unfortunately no transcripts of these meetings exist, the report prepared by the Codex Secretariat does not include details of proposals and comments or show how some interventions are "left by the wayside."

Codex:
WHO/FAO Told Nutrient Risk Assessment Must Consider Benefits

By Sepp Hasslberger
(Posted December 16, 2004)

In a submission to the FAO/WHO nutrient risk assessment project Dr. Robert Verkerk, Director of the Alliance for Natural Health charges that assessment of the possible risks of nutrient overdose must also consider the beneficial effects of nutrients. He says that risk assessments undertaken to date "are not based on a sufficiently rational scientific platform" and "will provide misleading information for policy decision-makers."

At stake is the continued availability of vitamin and mineral supplements for millions of consumers world wide who fear that the FAO's Codex Alimentarius guidelines may eventually establish dosage limits for such products that restrict their health choices. Limits would be based on scientific risk assessment but if the scientists do not consider all the data, including the benefits of nutrients and their immense value in achieving optimal health, the contemplated rules are likely to do more harm than good.

"There is a risk that key scientific data are ignored," says Verkerk in the ANH submission [download at, if the selection criteria are too rigid and exclude the wealth of experience with supplementation that has been gained in clinical nutrition, functional medicine and related disciplines. One of the points raised in the ANH submission was that the nutrient content in fruits and vegetables has been steadily declining since the introduction of "modern" agricultural methods and that therefore, supplementation is increasingly the only way to "top up" needed nutrients, let alone strive for optimal health.

Risk Assessment One-Sided -
Nutrients Need a Different Approach

Currently, risk assessment is geared to the toxicological evaluation of chemical poisons and other contaminants, which really have no place in our food supply. Nutrients are different, argues Verkerk and several others, in their submissions to the FAO project, seem to share this concern:

Lisa Intemann who pleads for low tolerance towards the chemical safety hazard posed by fluoride, echoes the ANH concerns when she points out the "essentially different nature of a non-Nutrient and Nutrient with respect to human physiology and risk management."

Michael-Anthony Seegers introduces a new concept when he says that "perhaps even more relevant to concerned sectors of society than a UL [upper level] is what I would call an OL or OPTIMUM LEVEL."

Gerd Stueckler goes even further. In a submission written in less than perfect but nevertheless perfectly understandable English, the German scientist perhaps best sums up the sentiments that are widely felt by consumers of supplements: The Codex legislative process and associated risk assessment work is seen as a threat to their health, an attempt to leave them without proper nutritional health support, rather than as a genuine effort to protect them. Some quotes from Stueckler's submission:

> "This is the first time in mankind's history that organizations like the FAO/WHO are trying to implement laws which will regulate and limit the access of the world's populations to nutrients and related substances. These laws would supersede all national laws of any country and would be enforced by the WTO. Any flaw within these laws would severely hamper any progress in the health and well being of the people world-wide. The resulting damage could easily become much more severe than the damage done to the people during all wars on

this planet.

The application of risk assessment procedures for hazardous chemicals and pharmaceuticals can never be applied to nutrients. The human organism is perfectly adapted since millions of years to all molecules which are part of used natural food nutrients - contrary to the artificial molecules of chemicals like pesticides and pharmaceuticals. This can be easily seen in the light of several hundred thousand deaths per year caused by correctly prescribed pharmaceuticals compared to virtually no deaths caused by nutrients from food or food supplements.

So the risk lies mostly in the lack of sufficient nutrients. All this leads to a completely different risk assessment procedure which must also take into consideration the many scientific discoveries of major health benefits of some nutrients (Vitamins, Minerals, etc.) when taking much higher doses of them [than] the average modern food provides.

Until the before mentioned issues regarding quality of scientific evidence are not principally and extensively solved there is not the slightest excuse left for the WHO not to immediately cease this Codex process.

When the WHO continues anyway on this fast track I must conclude that the whole Codex Alimentarius endeavor is not about protecting the world's public health but that it is only about protecting the profits of pharmaceutical companies and the profits of the health industry in general and that the WHO is willing to support the enforcement of a genocide on a world wide scale."

Dr. John Hathcock of the Council for Responsible Nutrition (CRN), who has proposed some of the current risk assessment methods, points out a flaw that is expected to lead to restrictions of the availability of niacin - Vitamin B3 to just 35 milligrams:

"Identification of an effect that qualifies as a "hazard" is a critical part of the UL risk assessment procedure. Effects may be undesirable but not qualify as a hazard.

An undesirable effect may in be only a nuisance when it is expected, but may be considered a hazard if it occurs unexpectedly. Niacin (as nicotinic acid) provides an excellent example:

1. *The vasodilative flushing reaction is undesirable but does not cause any known pathology. The EC SCF [European Community Scientific Committee on Foods] set its UL on the hypothetical possibility that vasodilation might cause positional hypotension and risk of falls, but did not cite any case in example. Notably, CRN (Hathcock 2004) has used the flushing effect to require a warning label at the level equal to the FNB UL [the US Food and Nutrition Board's Upper Level].*

2. *The data used by the FNB, SCF and EVM [the UK's Expert Group on Vitamins and Minerals] to derive UL values are of questionable relevance to foods or supplements. Those data were produced by giving bolus doses of free nicotinic acid to subjects with empty stomachs, thus maximizing the vasodilative potency of the nicotinic acid. The UL values derived from such data are apt to be unduly restrictive.*

3. *At much higher intakes than those that clearly cause flushing, nicotinic acid can cause liver and/or gastrointestinal pathology. Clinical trial data indicate a LOAEL [Lowest Observed Adverse Event Level] of 1,000 mg and a NOAEL [No Observed Adverse Event Level] of 500mg for these effects. These effects obviously would qualify as hazards and therefore be appropriate endpoints for nicotinic acid risk assessment.*

4. *The flushing effect may be the appropriate basis for a UL for products without a warning label (such as conventional foods and most manufactured foods). On the other hand, products, such as supplements, that can carry a flush warning label could have a UL based on the liver/gastrointestinal effects."*

CRN's Dr. Hathcock also criticizes the science used to justify calls for overly restrictive dosage limits on products containing Vitamin B 6, some of them as low as 10 milligrams:

> "The differences in data selection and the uncertainties of extrapolation are well illustrated in the FNC, SCF and EVM risk assessment on pyridoxine (vitamin B-6). All risk assessments agreed that excessive intakes of pyridoxine can cause a sensory neuropathy that only slowly or perhaps incompletely recovers. The differences in evaluation of pyridoxine data are summarized below:
>
> • FNB considered the long-term uses of high-dose pyridoxine in subjects who were monitored by physical neurology methods to be sufficient and most appropriate for the setting of the pyridoxine UL. In contrast, the FNB considered the survey data on Dalton and Dalton (1986) to be of such low scientific quality as to not be an appropriate basis for the UL.
>
> • SCF recognized the limitation of the Dalton and Dalton data but nonetheless used it as the basis of the UL. The UL was calculated from the median adverse effect level and an uncertainty factor of 4.0.
>
> • EVM considered all the human data to be of insufficient quality and therefore identified a UL (SUL in EVM terminology) from animal (dog) data through application of a composite uncertainty factor of 300 to the NOAEL. For pyridoxine, the EVM considered the high quality of the animal data and poor quality of the human data to warrant acceptance of the uncertainty of extrapolation between species . . ."

A comment from the chemical industry in the person of Dr. Klaus Kraemer of BASF, argues that regulation should be left to industry, citing the example of the GRAS [Generally Regarded As Safe] classification of food ingredients, which he says is working well in the U.S.:

> "The concept of "GRAS," as found in the food additive definition (US Food Drug and Cosmetic Act, Section 201(s)), provides a touchstone for a discussion since this has worked effectively for decades and has broad support and credibility among the scientific and regulated industry

communities.

Under a contract with the US FDA, the Food Nutrition Board (FNB) of the National Academies of Science Institute of Medicine (IOM) initiated a project "Dietary Supplements: A Framework for Evaluating Safety." In April 2004, the FNB published the framework for evaluating dietary supplement ingredients. The framework for evaluating the safety, outlines a science-based process for assessing supplement ingredients, even when data about a substance's safety in humans is scarce. The framework includes a methodology to review the available peer-reviewed literature with regard to the role of the dietary supplement ingredients in health, taking into consideration methods other expert bodies have used to categorize and review supplement safety and efficacy issues.

The use of any of these panels or variation of these could be an efficient means of providing the finest and most critical evaluation of the safety of new dietary ingredients for dietary peer-reviewed journals as critical reviews. GRAS determinations and supporting information would be submitted to the respective regulatory bodies as part of a review process. In this way, more credibility is added and consumer confidence is improved, and the regulators having the distinct advantage of having the final decision on the entry of new dietary ingredients to the market."

It appears unlikely that the FAO's risk assessment project would follow such a suggestion of industry self-regulation, but the thought is an interesting one to entertain. Perhaps no regulatory action is really needed for supplements because of their excellent safety record.

What really does seem urgently needed though is a general stock-taking of the benefits of nutritional intervention, something that has been neglected because of allopathic medicine's and therefore regulatory science's insistence on the prevalence of pharmaceutical, rather than nutrition-based health intervention. Only when the benefits of supplemental nutrition are "on the table", can we really weigh the possible dangers of nutrient overdose in a reasonable and accurate way.

Looks Like the EU Outmaneuvered the U.S.

By Suzan Walter
(posted on the AHHA website 2005)

International trade regulations for vitamin and mineral supplements are scheduled for finalization in July 2005. These could have been modeled after the lenient United States' approach. However, retracing events of the last fifteen years reveals how the EU tenaciously fought the U.S. every step of the way to emerge victorious in getting their restrictive rules as the international standard.

For three years I have been compiling information in an attempt to understand the controversy over the *Codex Draft Guidelines for Vitamin and Mineral Food Supplements (the Guidelines)*. Gaining insight into the different perspectives wasn't enough to explain why this international document related to dietary supplements was so important and the motivation behind the tenacity of some parties to get their way.

Then I learned a key fact that made so many other facts fall into place. The European Union (EU) is close to implementing an EU Pharmaceuticals Directive, which takes the position that anything that changes or enhances human physiology needs to be controlled as a **medicinal product**. This includes items that might prevent disease. Stop and consider the vast range of what this covers. The EU has a powerful agenda at stake with this Directive.

I had been comparing the Codex *Guidelines* and the EU Food Supplements Directive and trying to understand why it was so important to the EU that these be similar. Only when I stepped back and placed these documents within a larger context that included the EU Pharmaceuticals Directive did I grasp the significance.

Only then did the very short "positive list" of vitamins and minerals allowed by the EU Food Supplements Directive make sense. In EU countries, with so many dietary supplements regulated as medicinal products under the strict definition in the EU Pharmaceuticals Directive, there would be very few nutrients left over to be regulated by the EU Food Supplements Directive, and these would need to be at very low, ineffective dosage levels. Any supplement dosage high enough to benefit a human being would shift that product into the drug category.

Place this information in the context of the Codex Alimentarius, which provides food-related international trade standards that all countries can be forced to adopt through the enforcement powers of the World Trade Organization (WTO). You can see why it was vital to the EU that the Codex *Guidelines* be in alignment with the EU Food Supplements Directive. You can understand why the EU representative was motivated to fight so vigorously to add "Food" to the *Guidelines'* title and keep out any mention that vitamins and minerals might have any health benefits. And why he was particularly fervent to block any mention that vitamins and minerals could prevent disease.

If the Codex *Guidelines* had ended up lenient, there would be the potential that international harmonization could force the EU to give up its strict regional control of maintaining low levels of vitamin and mineral supplements as food and higher levels as drugs. To protect its interests the EU must keep the *Guidelines* and other Codex standards restrictive and in alignment with its Directives.

With this new understanding in mind, I retraced the history of the development of the Codex *Guidelines* looking for signs of the EU's strategy. I found that the idea to control dietary supplements had been first openly discussed at the 1988 session of an EU country-based Codex committee, the Codex Committee on Nutrition and Foods for Special Dietary Uses (CCNFSDU). Through the years, the EU representative to this committee kept successfully positioning the developing EU Food Supplements Directive ideas as core elements of the Codex Guidelines. The EU representative made a big issue of the fact that he was speaking for fifteen countries. This large EU block of "votes" in the CCNFSDU and other Codex sessions worked.

Where was the U.S. as this unfolded? CCNFSDU reports show that initially the U.S. protested the regulation of dietary supplements as inconsistent with U.S. national regulations. The U.S. said that regulation would unnecessarily restrict consumer access to dietary supplements. When this did not work, the U.S. did not, however, propose an alternative agenda. Rather, the FDA-led U.S. delegation constantly compromised its views and ended up accepting what the EU wanted. In fairness, it should be pointed out that the EU had the benefit of a block of "votes" and the sympathetic CCN-FSDU Chair from Germany (an EU country) declaring group consensus (approval) for whatever the EU supported.

What could the U.S. have proposed? Like the EU, the U.S. has a definition for health-enhancing products that can designate them as drugs. However, in the early 1990s the U.S. Dietary Supplement Health and Education Act (DSHEA) was passed. It designated vitamins, minerals, herbs, and many other dietary supplements as food, rather than drugs. There is no indication that any individual, group, or U.S. government entity felt motivated to encourage the rest of the world to follow suit. Therefore, without significant opposition, a commitment to prevail and effective use of the Codex system were powerful keys to success for the EU agenda.

With all of this in mind, take a fresh look at the various sections of the Codex Guidelines to see just how successful the EU has been:

- The document is titled *Codex Draft Guidelines for Vitamin and Mineral* **Food** *Supplements*.
- The Preamble states that a normal diet provides all the nutrients you need. There is no mention that supplemental nutrition can enhance health and prevent disease -- even in the face of a World Health Organization (WHO) publication documenting these facts. And the WHO is a *parent organization* of the Codex Alimentarius.
- We do not know which vitamins and minerals will be allowed, but numerous restrictive criteria are included.
- We do not know what dosage levels will be allowed, but several layers of options for lowering them are available.
- We do not know exactly how these unknowns will be determined or who will have the power to make these

decisions, but sympathetic FAO/WHO bodies have been
set up to produce results preferred by the EU.

In short, while we know the Codex *Guidelines* will be restrictive, we do not actually know what this document will specifically
allow. And yet the Guidelines document is on the agenda for finalization by the Codex Alimentarius Commission at the July 4-9,
2005, session in Rome.

Once the Guidelines are finalized -- whether in July 2005 or at
some future date -- will the EU be satisfied to let the U.S. be an isolated haven that allows unrestricted consumer access to high-
potency dietary supplements? Probably not. Understandably, the
EU will want to secure its powerful regional position and will most
likely look to removing any influence from the lenient U.S.
DSHEA law. This could be done very readily by having an EU
country file a trade dispute with the WTO against the U.S., nam-
ing something related to the differences between Codex and U.S.
supplement regulations. The WTO Dispute Settlement Panel
would compare the restrictive Codex *Guidelines* and the lenient
U.S. DSHEA regulations looking for an unfair trade advantage
and/or non-harmonization with international trade standards.
Since the WTO historically makes decisions that will level the
trade playing field, there would be a high probability that the WTO
would rule against the U.S. and direct the U.S. to revise DSHEA
to match the Codex *Guidelines*. And the U.S. would have to pay an
expensive trade sanction every year until it knuckled under and
changed DSHEA. Could the U.S. just refuse to pay? It may take
years, but the WTO keeps after a losing country until it does what
the WTO demands. Historically, the U.S. has changed its laws.

Should this happen, and DSHEA regulations were modified to
be as restrictive as the Codex *Guidelines* are ultimately expected to
be, would you be able to continue to freely purchase the wide range
of dietary supplements at your local health food store? Based on
what is already happening in several European countries, *probably
not*. Could the WTO really use economics to pressure the U.S. to
its will? A review of trade agreements signed by the U.S. shows
that it definitely could.

What can be done to protect your interests? Is it too late?
There aren't any easy answers. Advocacy groups in the U.S have

tried for years, but they have consistently found it difficult to generate concern. Americans have confidence in their government's ability to protect their rights and freedoms. They cannot believe that there are outside organizations (like the WTO) with more power than the U.S. government. Yet, my research has verified that the WTO has forced our country to change U.S. laws in the past.

I am sharing the facts I have uncovered in hopes that you will be better informed and more vigilant for positive actions to protect health freedoms in the U.S., particularly from the power of outside trade regulations. Remember the strong motivation of many other countries to restrict access to health-enhancing options, such as dietary supplements. These countries have become skilled in using international organizations to support their preferences. You can increase awareness of this serious matter by talking about this with your friends and colleagues. If you hear about advocacy campaigns for protecting health freedoms, listen. If you agree with their ideas, support what they are suggesting. Complacency supports and encourages those working to undermine the current heath freedoms in the U.S.

"There is nothing more frightful than ignorance in action."
- Johann Wolfgang von Goethe

Codex Guidelines History (1987-2004)

By Suzan Walter

(Posted in June 2005 on AHHA website)

The *Codex Draft Guidelines for Vitamin and Mineral Food Supplements (Guidelines)* document is on the agenda for finalization by the Codex Alimentarius Commission (CAC) at the July 2005 session in Rome. Some may find tracing the history of the drafting of this document enlightening.

Codex committee reports are not available online prior to 1996. However, when Suzan Walter was researching the *Guidelines* in 2002, Alan Randall of the Codex office in Rome provided general report excerpts indicating that the comments related to food supplements first appeared in the German-hosted Codex Committee on Nutrition and Foods for Special Dietary Uses (CCNFSDU) session report for 1988. The report did not identify which delegations proposed this work.

The 1988 start is verified by the 1989 CAC Session 18 Report when it mentions that the CCNFSDU had been discussing vitamin and mineral supplement products and the need for controls. In 1992, the CCNFSDU session report stated that the initial working draft was prepared by Germany.

Important background data: In some countries dietary supplement products are treated as pharmaceutical preparations (drugs), while in others they are "freely available" to the general public. Most countries allowing the public free access to vitamins and mineral supplements (including the U.S.) went on record against developing this type of guideline, as the restrictive controls would be "inconsistent with their national regulations and would unnecessarily restrict consumer access to dietary supplements." Their position that "there was no scientific basis for such restriction" did not withstand the power of those countries which felt "unregulated usage of some supplements might harm the health of consumers." Thus, the CCNFSDU was authorized to proceed to *protect the public and remove trade barriers*.

Once the project was set in motion, a number of issues became evident. In 1998, the European Union (EU) mentioned at the CCNFSDU session that the EU was drafting a paper dealing with these same issues. The Chair (from Germany) assigned Canada, the U.S. and the EU to study this EU paper and create a CCNFS-DU discussion paper on how the EU paper could be used in drafting the *Guidelines*. It should be noted that the EU paper went on to become the European Union Dietary Supplement Directive, which is extremely restrictive.

The official decision to proceed with developing the *Guidelines* appears to have been made at the 2000 CCNFSDU session. At this same session the CCNFSDU discussion paper assigned in 1998 (based on the EU directive) became the basis for a significant amount of the content of the *Guidelines*. This may account for the similarities between the two documents.

From the beginning the most controversial issue was how to determine the maximum amount of a vitamin or mineral to be allowed in a supplement product. Eventually the approaches being considered came down to two: (1) 100% of RDI (Recommended Daily Intake), or (2) upper limits to be based on a combination of risk assessment, including all dietary sources, and safety factors. The latter finally won out in 2003.

The issue of some countries designating dietary supplements as *food* and some as drugs was eventually addressed by having the *Guidelines* only apply to those countries using the food designation. Even the name of the document was revised to add the word "Food."

Having *positive* and *negative* lists, as the EU Dietary Supplement Directive uses to control which products would be legally allowed, was not incorporated into the *Guidelines*. Rather, 3.1.1 of the *Guidelines* states "Vitamin and mineral food supplements should contain vitamins/provitamins and minerals whose nutritional value for human beings has been proven by scientific data and whose status as vitamins and minerals is recognized by FAO and WHO." Interesting to note that there is no official list of FAO/WHO recognized vitamin and minerals.

The limited role of vitamin and mineral supplements, as defined in the Preamble of the *Guidelines*, went through challenges throughout the entire process of creating this document. Each attempt was unsuccessful. In 1998, the argument tried was that scientific data indicated that "diet may not be sufficient to meet the requirements for some nutrients of some population subgroups." In 2002 attempts were made to add mention of "prevention to reduce risk of disease." The EU led the objection based on it was not the committee's mandate "to consider the prevention, treatment or cure of diseases." In 2003, the attempt to mention prevention was declined based on the position that the Codex General Guidelines on Claims prohibited this. In 2004, the Chair would not allow the matter to be addressed. The final Preamble states "In cases where the intake from the diet is insufficient or where consumers consider their diet requires supplementation, vitamin and mineral food supplements serve to supplement the daily diet."

The intended use of the *Guidelines* would appear to be optional, based on the 2003 CCNFSDU session report that included replacing all uses of shall with should as "the text was not a standard." Twice at the 2004 CCNFSDU session it was stated from the podium that the Guidelines were optional. No mention was made to the delegates that Codex Alimentarius agreements with the World Trade Organization (WTO) would allow the WTO to use any Codex document (standard or guideline) as a mandatory trade standard to resolve international trade disputes.

If you wish further exploration into the history of the development of the *Guidelines*, you can review actual Codex reports and reports from participants. Links to these are available below.

# LINKS TO OFFICIAL CODEX REPORTS:
CAC = Codex Alimentarius Commission
CCNFSDU = Codex Committee on Nutrition and Foods for Special Dietary Uses

1987
CAC Session 17
[http://www.fao.org/docrep/meeting/005/ac319e/ac319e00.htm]
Paragraph 454: The former Codex Committee on Foods for Special Dietary Uses was renamed as Codex Committee for Nutrition and Special Dietary Uses - "in order to take into account the extended terms of reference as approved by the 15th Session of the Commission." No mention of Vitamins and Minerals.

1988
CCNFSDU Session
According to Alan Randall of Codex office in Rome - The process started in 1988 when "Several delegations" at the Codex Committee on Nutrition and Foods for Special Dietary Uses proposed work in the area of food supplements as part of an overall review of the work of Codex in the area of nutrition.

1989
CAC Session 18
[http://www.fao.org/docrep/meeting/005/t0236e/t0236e00.htm]
Vitamin and Mineral Supplements at Paragraphs 369 through 371
"The Commission was informed that the Committee had considered the need for standardization of these products (¶ 37, ALINORM 89/26). However, the Committee had doubts as to whether vitamin or mineral supplements would fall within the terms of reference of the Commission and had requested the Commission to consider this matter. The Chairman of the Committee indicated that in some countries these products were considered foods, while in others they were considered to be pharmaceutical preparations. Furthermore, depending on composition and other factors, these products could be either regarded as foods or pharmaceuticals. In any case, they were nutrient preparations serving a special dietary purpose." "Opinion was divided concerning the need to develop Codex standards for these products. Some delegations considered

that trade in these products was considerable and that Codex standards or guidelines should be developed to control them. Other delegations were of the opinion that there was no need, at this time, to work in this area. The point was made that a clear definition should be developed as to which products were foods and which products were to be considered pharmaceuticals." "The Commission agreed that the Secretariat should send a circular to governments seeking their views on whether or not work on vitamin and mineral supplements should be undertaken and to provide appropriate information so that distinction could be made between products which are foods and those which are pharmaceuticals or medicines. The Codex Committee on Nutrition and Foods for Special Dietary Uses was requested to consider information received and advise the Commission accordingly, without initiating the standardization of the products."

According to Alan Randall of Codex office in Rome - In 1989, the Codex Commission asked for more consultation between Member countries before agreeing to undertake the work. Identified the problem of defining supplements as "food" (i.e., falling within the Codex mandate) or as pharmaceuticals.

1991
CCNFSDU Session
According to Alan Randall of Codex office in Rome - In 1991 following a Circular Letter to Members, the Committee agreed to undertake work on guidelines for vitamin and mineral supplements, support ranging from a non-committal "not opposed" (Denmark) to "strong" (USA). The Commission later in the year approved the new work.

1991
CAC Session 19
[http://www.fao.org/docrep/meeting/005/t0490e/t0490e00.html]
Vitamin and Mineral Supplements at Paragraphs 272 through 274. "The Commission recalled its earlier decision to seek the views of governments on whether or not work on vitamin and mineral supplements should be undertaken within the Codex System, and to provide appropriate information so that distinction could be made between products which are foods and those which are pharmaceu-

tical or medicines." "The Commission noted that the comments received in response to this request had been discussed at the 17th Session of the Codex Committee on Nutrition and Foods for Special Dietary Uses. Most of the comments stressed the need to clearly distinguish between foods and drugs, and there was a general support for the development of guidelines. Several delegations at the present Session expressed support for the development of the document in view of the increasing international trade in these products and their free availability to the general public. Two delegations proposed that the *Guidelines* be further developed to cover other supplements such as amino acids, fatty acids. One delegation expressed concern over the implications of the Guidelines in those countries where these products are considered medicines." "The Commission noted the general support for a document on this subject and agreed that work on the Guidelines should continue. The Commission noted that a paper on vitamin and mineral supplements would be presented at the next session of the Codex Committee on Nutrition and Foods for Special Dietary Uses."

1992
CCNFSDU Session
According to Alan Randall of Codex office in Rome - In 1992, the initial working draft was prepared by Germany and circulated for comment.

1993
CAC Session 20
[http://www.fao.org/docrep/meeting/005/t0817e/t0817e00.htm]
Vitamin and Mineral Supplements at Paragraphs 293 through 294. "The Commission noted that the Committee, at its 18th Session, had considered the Guidelines for Dietary Supplements with Special Reference to Vitamins and Minerals. The Guidelines would be further considered by the Committee taking into account recent research information on vitamins and minerals and the fact that more and more supplementary products were available on the market." "The Observer of AOAC informed the Commission that an AOAC Manual containing methods of sampling and analysis of vitamins and minerals for use for nutrition Labeling purposes would be available in September."

1995
CAC Session 21
[http://www.fao.org/docrep/meeting/005/v7950e/v7950e00.htm]
No mention of Vitamin and Mineral Supplements.

1996
CCNFSDU Session
Report for Proposed Draft Guidelines for Dietary Supplements -- Agenda Item 7
[http://www.fao.org/docrep/meeting/005/w3663e/w3663e0a.htm#bm10]
Paragraphs 42 through 62.
Status of Guidelines document
[http://www.fao.org/docrep/meeting/005/w3663e/w3663e0j.htm#bm19.6]
Lead U.S. Delegate Dr. Elizabeth A. Yetley
The U.S., United Kingdom, and Japan were against developing the guidelines as the provisions therein were inconsistent with their national regulations and would unnecessarily restrict consumer access to dietary supplements. Others felt a need to regulate these "widely traded products." Canada emphasized the importance of applying risk-assessment methodology if setting maximum levels of intake. The Netherlands was for a safety-based approach in setting upper limits. There was agreement to concentrate on safety considerations based on scientific evidence and to change from "Dietary Supplements" to "Vitamin and Mineral Supplements." Added that guidelines would not apply where supplements were designated as drugs. Between a "positive list" and "no limitations should be set except on the basis of safety," decided to include only vitamins/provitamins and those minerals which were recognized as essential on a scientific basis.

1997
CAC Session 22
[http://www.fao.org/docrep/W5979e/W5979e00.htm]
Proposed Draft Guidelines for Vitamin and Mineral Supplements
Paragraphs 110 through 112.
"The Delegations of Canada and the United States, supported by Australia and Japan, expressed their objection to the development of the Guidelines in the framework of Codex as this matter should

be left to national authorities to regulate, in view of the wide differences between countries concerning the regulatory status and consumption habits of vitamin and mineral supplements. The development of international guidelines in this area would negatively affect the right of consumers to use these products, and there was no scientific basis for such restriction. It was also pointed out that many sections of the text were in square brackets and there may not be sufficient consensus at this stage to advance it to Step 6." "Several delegations pointed out that these products were traded internationally and their unregulated development posed a problem to control authorities, it was therefore essential that work on this issue should continue within the Committee on Nutrition and Foods for Special Dietary Uses."

1997
CCNFSDU Session
According to Alan Randall of Codex office in Rome - In 1997, the Proposed Draft Guidelines submitted to the 22nd Session of the Codex Commission for consideration and approval (Step 5) and the Commission returned it to the Committee for re-drafting due to lack of consensus on the content of the guidelines.

1998
CCNFSDU Session
Report for Proposed Draft Guidelines for Vitamin and Mineral Supplements -- Agenda Item 5
[http://www.fao.org/docrep/meeting/005/x0204e/x0204e0a.htm#bm10]
Paragraphs 41 through 48.
Document not provided
Lead U.S. Delegate Dr. Elizabeth A. Yetley
Strong opinions that guidelines needed to be developed as "unregulated usage of some supplements might harm the health of consumers." "Moreover, since national legislation could not always address the problems and trade barriers already existed, it was essential to provide an international reference in the framework of the Codex and to ensure fair trade practices." Canada (supported by the U.S.) "strongly objected to further elaboration of the guidelines as this would interfere with the trade of products which could benefit certain consumers, as recent scientific data [10] indicate

that diet may not be sufficient to meet the requirements for some nutrients of some population subgroups; in addition, many consumers felt that the consumption of vitamin and minerals was a "right," and products which were safe and presented no health risk should be freely available. The Delegation stressed that, since the attitude and perception of consumers greatly differed from one country to another, the regulation of supplements should be left to national authorities." Debate on upper limits included an approach combining risk assessment, considering all dietary sources, and safety factors. The EU proposed that a paper on dietary supplements being developed by the EU could serve to revolve several unresolved issues. A discussion paper on several issues, to be based on the EU paper, was assigned to Canada, the U.S., and the EU.

1999
CAC Session 23
[http://www.fao.org/docrep/meeting/005/x2630e/x2630e00.html]
No mention of Vitamin and Mineral Supplements.

2000
CCNFSDU Session
Report for Proposed Draft Guidelines for Vitamin and Mineral Supplements -- Agenda Item 5
[http://www.fao.org/docrep/meeting/005/x2630e/x2630e00.html]
Paragraphs 36 through 57.
Status of Guidelines document
[http://www.fao.org/docrep/meeting/005/x7839e/x7839e0q.htm#bm26]
Lead U.S. Delegate Dr. Elizabeth A. Yetley

The discussion paper assigned in 1998 to Canada, the U.S., and the EU was introduced by the U.S. First, the discussion addressed whether or not to proceed with the elaboration of the Guidelines. Canada, India, and Kenya strongly objected. The U.S. stressed the importance of consumer choice and access to vitamin and mineral supplements. Malaysia and others felt it was necessary to regulate products in the marketplace that sometimes had a very high dosage of vitamins and minerals in order to avoid misleading consumers. The decision was to proceed. Then each section of the Guidelines was addressed in conjunction with the Discussion paper. It was agreed that "supplements should contain substances of nutritive value proven by scientific data, instead of indispensability in Section 3.1.1." "Section 3.1.2 was amended to reflect that criteria such as safety and bioavailability were essential in the selection of sources . . . ." No consensus on minimum and maximum levels. Extensive debate, also, on the declaration of vitamins and minerals. Some supported reference to the biologically active part of vitamins and minerals as bioavailability was referenced as one of the criteria in Section 3 while other delegations indicated that the meaning of this wording was not clear enough. As a compromise it was agreed to amend the former Section 8.3 as proposed by the Observer of the EC and including the references to amounts of vitamins and minerals by units of weight, the amount per portion of the product and the percentage of the NRV mentioned and retained it in square brackets.

2001
CAC Session 24
No mention of Vitamin and Mineral Supplements

2001
CCNFSDU Session
Report for Proposed Draft Guidelines for Vitamin and Mineral Supplements -- Agenda Item 4
Paragraphs 18 through 40
Status of Guidelines document on page 41 in Appendix II
Lead U.S. Delegate Dr. Elizabeth A. Yetley
Noted that "the current Guidelines contained some prescriptive text that could be more relevant to a standard." Option to extend scope of Guidelines to cover herbs was not accepted, as this matter is to be left to national authorities to decide. Section 3. Composition was amended to make less prescriptive, plus stated that the status of vitamins and minerals should be recognized by FAO/WHO. Lower limits of 15%, 25% and 33% were discussed. Upper limits continue to be between 100% of recommended daily intake vs. risk assessment and considering all sources of the nutrients.

2002
CCNFSDU Session
Report for Proposed Draft Guidelines for Vitamin and Mineral

Supplements -- Agenda Item 6
Paragraphs 87 through 100.
Status of Guidelines document on page 56 in Appendix IV
Lead U.S. Delegate Dr. Elizabeth A. Yetley
The Chair stressed the importance of a risk-based approach and the work of FAO and WHO on establishment of safe upper limits. Added "food" to title to clarify that the products were foods at request of EU. South Africa and the National Health Federation supported revising Preamble to include reference to prevention to reduce risk of disease. EU and others objected to as not mandate of committee "to consider the prevention, treatment or cure of diseases." No progress on criteria for upper limits.

2003
CAC Session 26
No mention of CCNFSDU.

2003
CCNFSDU Session
Report for Proposed Draft Guidelines for Vitamin and Mineral Supplements -- Agenda Item 5
Paragraphs 36 through 61.
Status of Guidelines document on page 44, Appendix IV.
Lead U.S. Delegate Dr. Elizabeth A. Yetley
Efforts to block addition of "food" to title unsuccessful. South Africa tried to get preventive role of vitamins and minerals added to Preamble. This was declined based on position that General Guidelines on Claims prohibited it. Efforts to remove reference to whether countries referred to vitamins and minerals as food or drugs were unsuccessful. Sentence states Guidelines to be applied to foods. EC successfully proposed to add provisions so that food supplements containing vitamins and mineral were also subject to Guidelines. Specified that the purpose of products "is to supplement the intake of vitamins and/or minerals from the normal diet." Minimum amount set at 15%. Upper limits were finally resolved on "the basis of scientific risk assessment." Rather then child-resistant packages, labeling is to specify that "the product should be stored out of reach of young children." Name of product should be "food supplements." Each place shall appeared, it was replaced

with should as "the text was not a standard." Need for a "warning statement" was replaced with "advice to the consumer not to exceed the maximum one-day amount." A requirement that "supplements should be taken on the advice of a nutritionist, a dietician or a medical" was removed.

2004
CAC Session 27
No mention of CCNFSDU.

2004
CCNFSDU Session
Report for Proposed Draft Guidelines for Vitamin and Mineral Food Supplements -- Agenda Item 4
Paragraphs 23 through 35.
Status of Guidelines document on page 42 in Appendix II
Lead U.S. Delegate Dr. Barbara O. Schneeman
The Chair commented again about prior agreement to refer to vitamin and mineral "food" supplements in title and relevant parts of document. Quantity reference ended up "to be taken in measured small-unit quantities" and added a footnote to clarify reference is to physical forms of vitamin and mineral supplements. Finalized "selection should be based on considerations of safety and bioavailability." Recalled that agreed earlier to "limit guidelines to vitamin and minerals for which the Recommended Daily Intake was established by FAO/WHO." Agreed to advance the Draft Guidelines for adoption at Step 8 by 28th Session of the Codex Alimentarius Commission.

Summer of '05
Critical Time for Dietary
Supplements

By Suzan Walter

The future of dietary supplements may be determined by what happens this Summer. Not just one, but many different yet related matters are all coming to a head during the Spring and Summer months of 2005. Since everything is interrelated, you will want to track national, regional, and international events.

When you review articles and e-mails dealing with supplements (and there are a number making the rounds), it is important that you understand the impact of each of these events individually, as well as collectively. The following review is presented to assist you in understanding the nuances of each issue and in recognizing when some sources blur and confuse the distinctions.

Codex Guidelines for Vitamin and Mineral Food Supplements

The Codex Guidelines for Vitamin and Mineral Food Supplements is an international document drafted to be guidelines for vitamin-and-mineral supplement products. It states that it is only for countries that designate these supplements as food, exempting countries that designate supplements as drugs. Last November, after over a decade of wrangling over numerous supplement regulation issues, a Codex committee completed an eight-step process that created the official Guidelines document. Finalization of the Guidelines document is on the agenda for the Rome July 4-9, 2005 session of the top Codex body, the Codex

Alimentarius Commission. At this time, there does not appear to be anything that can be done to stop this final action. Under Codex authority, these Guidelines are optional suggestions, not a mandatory trade standard that must be followed in trade between countries.

However, there are agreements between Codex Alimentarius and the World Trade Organization that allow the WTO to use Codex documents (such as the Guidelines) as mandatory international trade standards to settle trade disputes. The WTO can enforce dispute decisions by pressuring the losing country through trade sanctions if they do not change their national laws or other regulations to conform to international trade standards. Therefore, the regulations in the Guidelines must be taken seriously.

The section of the Guidelines expected to have the most significant impact is the criteria by which the maximum amounts of vitamins and minerals that will be allowed in a supplement product are determined. The Guidelines state that ". . . upper safe levels of vitamins and mineral established by scientific risk assessment based on generally accepted scientific data . . . ." As there is currently no generally accepted scientific risk-assessment protocol available, what these limits will be is unknown. Some individuals are very concerned that the upper limits will be set too low. This could mean that instead of one convenient high-dosage capsule, the consumer might need to take a handful of low-dosage capsules.

FAO Risk-Assessment Protocol

The Food and Agriculture Organization (FAO) of the United Nations and the World Health Organization (WHO) announced in December 2004, that they were accepting applications from individuals who wish to serve as the experts on a joint nutrient risk-assessment project to define a scientifically-based nutrient risk assessment. Work is scheduled to begin in May 2005. The balance of perspectives of the experts selected will be the first sign of how this project will progress. It is anticipated, but not guaranteed, that this nutrient risk-assessment protocol will be used to define the upper safe limits of the Codex Guidelines.

European Union Food Supplements Directive

The collection of countries making up the European Union (EU) will be severely impacted by the activation of the EU Food

Supplements Directive on August 1, 2005. The Directive is purported to provide reassurance for EU consumers that the ingredients used in food supplements have been thoroughly assessed for safety. There is a "positive list" that includes 28 vitamins and minerals that are deemed safe. After August 1, EU stores can legally only sell supplement products containing these ingredients. What is causing grave concerns, however, is the long list of 200 vitamins and minerals that did not make the "positive list." While a supplement would normally need to be proved dangerous to be removed from public consumption, the Directive works in just the opposite way. The supplement must be proved safe to get onto the "positive list" and be available to the EU consumer. The process of proving that a vitamin or mineral is safe is very costly.

A number of groups are so concerned about the negative impact of the Directive that this matter has been taken to the regional courts in Europe. At a January 25, 2005, hearing the Alliance for Natural Health and Nutri-Link Ltd presented their arguments that the EU is exceeding its powers. An opinion will be released April 5, 2005, with the final decision expected in June, 2005. The decision will set a major precedent for the world, particularly if the EU Directive side loses.

DSHEA & Legislation in U.S.

The key legislative protection that gives consumers in the United States access to dietary supplements is the Dietary Supplement Health and Education Act of 1994 (DSHEA). A number of senators and and members of congress in Washington are working to reverse some or all of these protections. Last year, in the 108th session of Congress, a number of bills were introduced that caused concern among those who use supplements. It is expected that these bills will be reintroduced in the current (109th) session in April-May time frame, with serious committee hearings in the following months. While the bill numbers will be different, the content is expected to be very similar. A few of the bills to watch for are:

- Dietary Supplement Safety Act (was S. 722). This bill would amend the Federal Food, Drug, and Cosmetic Act to require that manufacturers of dietary supplements submit to the FDA reports on adverse experiences with dietary supplements. Opponents question whether dietary supplements need to be held to a higher standard than drugs. Would it be fair to have a supplement taken off the market based on one negative reaction while a drug can remain available even as it harms many?

• Dietary Supplement Access and Awareness Act (was H.R. 3377). This bill would grant the FDA authority to regulate supplements in the same way that it regulates over-the-counter drugs. Opponents are concerned that this is working toward the day when you would need a doctor's prescription to get vitamin and mineral supplements.

• Safe Food Act of 2004 (was S. 2910). This bill would create a new federal food safety agency. Ten separate federal agencies handling various food matters would be combined into one. This sounds like an efficient administrative approach. However, the bill stated that the term "food" would not include dietary supplements. If not food, what's left? Drugs?

How these events are connected

Some of the connections between the events described above are obvious. However, there are some subtle relationships that are not as well known. Here are a few examples:

The EU has a very strong influence on decisions made in Codex committee sessions. In fact, the *Guidelines* document does not include a number of items because the EU delegate was vehemently against them. In one prominent example the delegate from South Africa tried on a number of occasions to get wording into the Preamble of the Guidelines to acknowledge that vitamins and minerals had preventive benefits. The EU delegate successfully objected every time. At this same Codex session the FAO/WHO publication, "Diet, Nutrition and the Prevention of Chronic Diseases" was being promoted on the literature table. Based on this demonstration of EU influence, many people believe that the EU Food Supplements Directive indicates what Codex documents might end up including in the future.

The United States Federal Register, October 11, 1995, FDA Policy on Standards, states that "where a relevant international standard exists, or completion is imminent, it will generally be used in preference to a domestic standard...." If this is still the FDA policy, once the Codex Guidelines are finalized this Summer, will we find the FDA working to use this against the DSHEA?

Have you noticed the growing number of situations where dietary supplement companies are being required to submit costly documentation to prove that a vitamin or mineral is safe, even when there is extensive research already demonstrating its safety and effectiveness? This is what is currently happening in Europe and Canada. The negative economic impact is changing the landscape of the entire industry. Are we seeing a scenario where small companies will either have to sell out to larger supplement companies or fold? Where many of the larger companies are being bought out by pharmaceutical companies? Do current events support the strength of the supplement companies or the pharmaceutical companies?

As you consider the difference between what is on the six o'clock news and what the health-freedom advocacy websites proclaim, evaluate for yourself what this difference might mean for you and those you love. Get involved with groups that support what you believe will be most beneficial.

If a nation values anything more than freedom, it will lose its freedom; and the irony of it is that if it is comfort or money that it values more, it will lose that too.

- William Somerset Maugham
in *Strictly Personal* (1941)

The Summer of our Discontent:

How the Codex Commission Lost Its Rulebook and the European Court of Justice Found Its Own

By Scott C. Tips

(Published in *Health Freedom News* Vol. 23, No. 3, Fall 2005 &
Whole Foods Magazine , Vol. 28, No. 9, September 2005)

*"Hell, there are no rules here –
we're trying to accomplish something."*
- Thomas Edison

By now, you will have heard the news: The Codex Alimentarius Commission, meeting in Rome, Italy on the 4th of July, approved the *Codex Guidelines on Vitamin and Mineral Food Supplements*. Amongst the hundreds present, only one lone voice argued against adoption – mine.

Not that there wasn't sympathetic support present, they just could not speak out. Many others who shared my opinion had journeyed even further than I to swelter in the unusually hot Roman sun, rub elbows with an army of anti-supplement bureaucrats, eat bland cafeteria food, and see what they could do to stop the juggernaut from crushing health freedom.

I attended this 28th Session of the Codex Alimentarius Commission as the head of the National Health Federation (www.thenhf.com) observer delegation, as usual the only pro-health-freedom organization able to speak out at these meetings. With me were a number of marvelous health-freedom fighters such as NHF Vice Chairman Paul Anthony Taylor, who was second-in-charge of our delegation, Tamara Thérèsa Mosegaard of MayDay, Sepp Hasslberger of La Leva, and Dr. Carolyn Dean of Friends of Freedom and also an NHF Board of Governors member. In turn, we were supported by others such as Friends of Freedom International's Trueman Tuck and Peter Helgason, the Coalition for Natural Health Freedom's Diane Miller, the Dr. Rath Foundation's Kathy Perry, and Citizens for Health's Jim Turner, who were in attendance either as public observers or members of country delegations but who had no public voice at Codex. All contributed, though, and deserve recognition for their contributions.

We basically hit the ground running that first morning because we knew that the draft Guidelines for Vitamin and Mineral Food Supplements, spat out of the Bonn Committee last November, was going to be up for approval no later than the end of the first day of the meeting, July 4th. Our group divided up assignments and we quickly lobbied various country delegations that we thought would be favorable to our view that the *Vitamin and Mineral Food Supplement Guidelines* should not be approved but should be sent back to the Bonn Committee for redrafting. I personally spoke with a number of country delegate heads, whom I shall not name here because this process is still ongoing, and received sympathetic responses. Others in our group got similar responses.

Australia Gets Strong-Armed First

But before we could finish, the meeting was quickly called to order by Commission Chairman Dr. Stuart Slorach and he got down to business. The first item that was of interest to the NHF was Agenda Item 4 involving a request by the delegation of Australia that certain language be left in the Codex Procedural Manual. At the last April committee meeting in Paris, the Codex Committee on General Principles, the Australians had surprisingly sought to save some language embedded in a vast amount of text that the Codex people had wanted to strike out about acceptance and rejection procedures that countries could undertake to either accept or reject Codex standards. Within that text was wording stating that, essentially, Codex standards are "not a substitute for or an alternative to national legislation." Australia wanted to retain that language in order to protect its drug regime governing vitamins and minerals. For completely opposite reasons, the NHF strongly supported Australia's position in order to clarify that Codex standards are not superior to national standards and thus help protect DSHEA in the United States.

Unfortunately, at the April committee meeting in Paris, the chairman decided that this hot potato could be passed upwards for consideration at the Commission level. Well, that day arrived very quickly on Monday, July 4th, and the chairman decided that the entire deletion – including the wording that Australia and the NHF had sought to save – should be approved, but then the chairman threw a scraggly bone to Australia by telling it that it could still raise that issue at next year's Paris committee meeting. Lucky Australia.

That's how they handle opposition at Codex meetings – at least one way they handle it – it's like an egg on the floor, you push it around until it disappears. The Paris committee had pushed this issue over opposition – as approved with everything deleted – up to the Commission level. The Commission then approved all deletions (again over opposition) and pushed it back down to the committee for further discussion by Australia, *if* it chooses to do so. But if Australia does choose to tackle this issue again, then the Paris committee chairman could probably argue that the Commission has already approved the entire deletion. Health freedom loses, and it did so this July with barely a whimper and a rollover from the Australian delegate. *"Nice boy, here's your bone,"* I almost expected to hear the Chairman say.

When I was finally recognized to speak at the end (by mistake I later learned), I raised some delegates' eyebrows when I supported the original Australian delegation position but said that I was disappointed that Australia had chosen to "cave in" on this issue. Evidently, non-governmental observer delegations, such as the NHF, are supposed to show "proper respect" for government employees. Funny, I always thought they worked for *us* and should show *us* respect. The Commission broke for lunch as I mulled this over.

Then, Consumers Get Bludgeoned

With the delegates sleepy from their nutrient-poor, pasta-rich meals, the Chairman began with Agenda Item 5, which was to consider a long list of many Codex guidelines up for approval by the Commission. It was obvious to all that the Chairman was hell-bent for leather to get every single one of those guidelines approved by the Commission, and in record time. He very quickly ran down the list, just as if he were literally going through a grocery list - a quick look at the item, an equally quick mention of it, and then a quick look up-and-around to make sure no one dared slow him down before he announced "approved!" A staccato rhythm of approval was quickly set.

When the Chairman reached the draft *Guidelines for Vitamin and Mineral Food Supplements*, the momentum slowed for just a moment as he dealt with some last-minute wording revisions sought by Australia, Venezuela, and China. The first two countries' revisions were ruled technical, while China's was determined by the Chairman to be substantive. The last ruling was important because under Codex procedural rules if a change sought by a country is substantive, then the guideline cannot be approved and **must** be sent back to its committee for re-review.

But sitting in the German delegation to this meeting was Dr. Rolf Grossklaus, the chairman of the Bonn Codex committee, who reminded the Swedish Chairman of how wonderful these *Guidelines* were. He spoke at length and directly to the Chairman, as if they had discussed this all before and he, unworried, were merely going through the motions.

Then, the Columbian delegate tried to speak and, after a technical problem with his microphone was resolved, was able to blurt out his message: vitamins are dangerous and should be stopped. Obviously he had never read Mark Twain's admonishment, "*It is better to keep your mouth shut and appear stupid than open it and remove all doubt.*"

After these countries were heard, the Chairman recognized me to speak out on the issue. Unfortunately, I was the sole voice **against** adoption of the draft *Guidelines* by the Commission. Arguing that they were defective and must be sent back to Committee, I gave three main reasons: (1) According to Codex's own Procedural Manual, guidelines must state a purpose for those guidelines in the Preface and the draft *Guidelines for Vitamin-and-Mineral Food Supplements* do not contain a purpose, (2) The *Guidelines* fail to define what vitamins and minerals are covered by the *Guidelines* since they refer to a nonexistent FAO/WHO list of approved vitamins and minerals and therefore it is unclear as to what would actually be covered by the *Guidelines*; and (3) The comments made by China, and the changes sought by China to the *Guidelines*, were substantive and according to the Codex Rules of Procedure as stated on page 27 of the Manual of Procedure, any substantive amendment *must* be sent back to the Committee and dealt with at the committee level.

After I spoke, during which time the Chairman never even once looked at me, none of the countries that we had expected to support our position did so, and there was nothing but silence from the floor. Then, the International Alliance of Dietary/Food Supplement Associations (IADSA) observer delegate was recognized to speak. He argued in favor of the adoption of the *Guidelines* because, believe it or not, the committee had spent ten "long" years working on them, so – in his view – they must be approved no matter how defective they were. Had he been alive when the Catholic Church was debating whether to end torture and the Spanish Inquisition in 1834, I suppose he would have argued against its abolition because of the 350 *long years* it had been operating.

Well, regardless, he got his wish because the Chairman ignored the blatant procedural defects, and with all of the countries silent on this issue, the Chairman simply acted in a very arbitrary manner. He brushed aside the substantiveness of the Chinese-requested changes, completely failed to address the issue of those defects, and decided on his own and by fiat that the *Guidelines* were adopted.

Curiously enough, throughout the rest of the week, neither the Chairman nor the FAO Secretariat later showed the least bit of inhibition in quoting from the Procedural Manual when it was in *their* interests to do so. The Chairman, who has since been replaced by a new person elected during this meeting, and the Secretariat must have lost their copies of the Manual and with it, their sense of justice. In 1943, U.S. Supreme Court Justice Felix Frankfurter noted in a court decision that the *"history of liberty has largely been the history of observance of procedural safeguards."* When the Chairman and the Secretariat lost their rulebook that afternoon, they let procedural safeguards slip away and with it freedom. The next time an issue like this arises, it will be even easier for them to forget procedural safeguards because habits will have been built upon habits. And, accustomed to that, no country delegate will object – just as none did here.

So, what is next? Come this Thanksgiving week, the *Guidelines* will be back before the Codex Committee in Bonn, Germany so that some of the blank spaces in it can start to be filled in – particularly applying the nutrient risk-assessment analysis that was agreed to two years ago to establish the maximum upper limits for vitamins and minerals. The NHF will be there again, this time with scientific advisors, to influence the debate.

As Sepp Hasslberger, a long-time Codex observer, has recently noted, "there is talk about 'risk assessment' but the name of the game is to *not* allow any supplements that would be useful over and above the 'food-physiological' handling of deficiencies." The Germans will dig in and seek to restrict vitamin-and-mineral potencies to no more than three times the RDA, if even that.

The challenge here will be to apply the more libertarian American model of risk assessment rather than the restrictive European model that is stridently anti-supplement. In that way, hope would exist for sanity. But the European stranglehold upon Codex is viciously tight. That must and will be changed.

The European Court of Justice

"Show me a thoroughly satisfied man
and I will show you a failure."
– Thomas Edison

The European Union's food-and-drug bureaucrats have consistently strived, and so far successfully, to make the *Codex Guidelines for Vitamin and Mineral Food Supplements* match -- virtually word for word --their own Food Supplements Directive.

In other words, Europe will soon be locked down tight with the Food Supplements Directive so that almost nothing that is useful in the form of vitamins or minerals will be legally sold within Europe. (Of course, a huge black market, unstoppable by the EU bureaucrats, will arise almost immediately.) Then, with the Codex *Guidelines* matching closely the Food Supplements Directive, they will prevent any lawful sales *into* Europe of the high-value, low-cost, superior American dietary supplements because that international trade, at the very least, will be prevented by the Codex *Guidelines* and its enforcement mechanism, the World Trade Organization.

The only thing that was standing in the European regulator's domestic path was the pan-European Alliance for Natural Health's excellently-managed lawsuit that was launched a few years ago against the Directive, with the aim of taking the case to the

European equivalent of the Supreme Court, the European Court of Justice. The ANH, and its fellow litigants, were successful in January 2004 in getting the London court to refer the case to the higher court - the European Court of Justice (ECJ) in Luxembourg.

I attended the hearing before the ECJ on the ANH's court case, which was held on January 26, 2005. (See "My Luxembourg Morning" *Whole Foods Magazine*, June 2005). At that hearing, the EU and certain supporting countries' legal counsel were a sad lot presenting even sadder arguments. Perhaps I am biased, but, in contrast, the ANH's attorney, Paul Lasok QC, did an outstanding job with his arguments. The ECJ even seemed somewhat sympathetic to ANH's case, as revealed by its hard questions asked of ANH's opponents. This view was supported by the Advocate General's preliminary and non-binding opinion, handed down last April 5, wherein he found the Directive invalid.

Then, with the Codex Commission showdown over the *Codex Guidelines* looming large on the horizon, most of us were expecting the ECJ decision to conform, as it usually does, to the Advocate General's preliminary opinion. Expectations were high for a favorable decision, set to be announced just after the Codex Commission finished its early July meeting in Rome.

On July 12th, the ECJ finally handed down its written decision and everyone, myself included, rushed to read the bottom line. Initially disappointing, the Court's decision failed to adopt the Advocate General's preliminary opinion and instead upheld the validity of the Directive. Years of hard work went seemingly unrewarded, except for one small comment made by the Court, almost offhandedly and in passing, earlier in the text. And then another . . . and then yet another.

Piecing them together, it became increasingly clear that the Court **had** not handed the regulators and their fellow travelers the victory that they were trumpeting. While the ECJ did not, in my opinion, make new law, it did state more clearly and precisely existing law. And that existing law is **not** favorable to the EU regulators, who have been misapplying the law for years. That is about to end for the following reasons:

1. The Directive distinguishes between vitamins and minerals used in food supplements that are manufactured from "chemical substances" and all other ingredients in food supplements that come from natural sources in foods. In making that distinction, the Court clearly states that those vitamins and minerals normally found in foods are not covered by the Directive or its ban. (Decision ¶ 63)

2. In those instances where it is necessary to apply to be on the positive list of permitted vitamins and minerals, the process will now be a much simpler, less time-consuming, and less-expensive undertaking than before. (Decision ¶¶ 72-91)

3. The burden of proof (and hence the greater part of the expense) for showing a food-supplement ingredient to be unsafe lies with the regulator and not the manufacturer. That ingredient cannot be refused unless and until the regulator proves it unsafe by undertaking a full risk/safety assessment based upon "the most reliable scientific data available and the most recent results of international research." (Decision ¶ 73, cited cases)

4. All of which in turn means that most vitamin-and-mineral food supplements on the markets in the EU will not been banned come August 1st, especially if they are outside the purview of the Directive because of being "naturally sourced."

Because, prior to this decision, the Directive has been vague and thus subject to bureaucratic interpretive whim, supplement manufacturers followed the *regulators'* view of how supplements should gain access to the positive list of vitamins and minerals that may be lawfully sold in Europe. That meant that both parties assumed that the manufacturer had to shoulder the burden of proof of safety and would have to spend, in many cases, more than £250,000 per supplement ingredient on a complex dossier submission to the food authorities. For natural, unpatented food products, such costs would be prohibitively expensive, especially for those companies with thirty or more ingredients to list.

Thanks now to the Alliance for Natural Health (www.alliance-natural-health.org) and its fellow plaintiffs, and thanks to a Court that follows procedure, that appears to no longer be necessary. Since the Court has ruled technically that the Directive only applies to those supplements manufactured from chemically derived substances and since the burden of proving safety has been clearly placed upon the regulators' shoulders within a system that must be more transparent, the dreaded death-grip of the Directive has been greatly reduced. That, then, would constitute a victory for ANH and the rest of us, even if the Directive was not struck down in its entirety.

However, it remains to be seen if the European Commission and some of the European governments will choose to interpret the ECJ's ruling accurately. They may decide to play by their own rules, in the hope that neither the ANH nor any other party will risk going back to court for a further challenge. One of the ironies in this is that it is quite likely that different countries will choose to make different interpretations of the ruling, thus upsetting the level of playing field that this harmonizing Directive was promising to offer.

In fact, as Dr. Robert Verkerk, Executive Director of the ANH, has commented, we should also be consoled in some ways that the Directive was not invalidated by the Court, probably largely as a result of a face-saving exercise on the part of the Court, that is, as a means of protecting the European institutions such as the European Commission and the European Food Safety Authority. Had the Directive been invalidated, then the ANH and a rash of competing interests would have had to lobby the European Commission and the Council of Ministers, made up of Health Ministers from the 25 European governments, and an amended proposal would then eventually be agreed upon. This would then be put before the European Parliament. If whatever emerged from the end of this complicated European law-making sausage machine had an effect that was similar to the ruling given now by the ECJ, then the ANH and many pro-health-freedom interests would have been quite happy. This ruling has avoided the need for this – the process has been fast-tracked, and the European Commission has not been embarrassed. Some would call this a win-win.

Dr. Verkerk has also noticed that the Court's placement of the burden of proving safety upon the regulators and not manufacturers suggests a similarity between the European Directive and the American Dietary Supplement Health and Education Act. This is an interesting concept and one to be explored further.

In the meantime, even with the Court's clarification of the Food Supplements Directive, many questions remain – such as, determining exactly the composition of the simplified procedures for getting ingredients onto the "positive list" and whether different European countries will accept those derogations that have been applied for in a different country than their own. So, too, those regulators who wish to preserve their view of the Directive will challenge the plaintiffs' interpretation of the Court ruling, almost certainly insisting that they may proceed as they planned. There will be further fights as the Directive's limits are defined and the regulators attempt to impose their interpretations instead.

But rather than be unhappy that the structure of the Directive was not brought down by this decision, we should be satisfied – but not thoroughly satisfied – that the Court had the wisdom to rein in the regulators. Those who hate and fear food supplements are rejoicing, seeing only the edifice of the Directive, which the Court has left standing. Overlooked, though, in their blind joy, is the bomb that the Court has exploded inside the structure, gutting it, and taking away half its backside. The dust is still settling.

The Worst is Still to Come

By Paul Anthony Taylor

(November 2005)

November 2005 saw the 27th meeting of the Codex Committee on Nutrition and Foods for Special Dietary Uses (CCNFSDU) take place in Bonn, Germany. The Committee, one of 27 currently active Codex committees, has been meeting in Germany since its inception in 1966, and was responsible for the drafting of the controversial *Guidelines for Vitamin and Mineral Food Supplements*. However, and as this article will show, the most potentially damaging aspects of the Committee's attacks on natural healthcare and health freedom are still to come.

The 2005 meeting of the Codex Committee on Nutrition and Foods for Special Dietary Uses (CCNFSDU) took place from 21-25 November, in Bonn, Germany, and was attended by 315 delegates representing 68 countries and 33 international organizations.

Any doubts as to whether or not Codex is concerned about its loss of trust and respect amongst consumers were immediately dispelled by the Committee's infamous Chairman, Dr. Rolf Grossklaus, who opened the meeting by stating that the Committee had to improve its public relations image. However, any hopes that Codex might be about to change course proved to be wide of the mark when he went on to announce that the Food and Agriculture Organization of the United Nations (FAO), one of the two Codex parent bodies, would be filming this year's meeting, and explained that as a part of the film the FAO filmmakers would be interviewing some of the delegates. Clearly therefore we can expect to see a particularly propaganda-laden film becoming available for viewing on the Codex Alimentarius website in due course, complete with Codex delegates talking gushingly and disingenuously about "protecting" consumers.

In addition, Dr. Grossklaus revealed that next year's CCNFS-DU meeting will be taking place not in Germany, but in Thailand. Perhaps not surprisingly, therefore, some delegates subsequently speculated, privately, that this change in venue might in part be due to the adverse publicity that has been generated by the work of the Committee in recent years and that by holding their next meeting in Thailand, away from the public gaze, the Committee might be hoping to avoid further damaging scrutiny of its work.

Four items on the Committee's agenda this year were of particular importance to the future of natural healthcare and health freedom.

Proposals for Additional or Revised Nutrient Reference Values (NRVs) for Labeling Purposes

The proposal to consider additional or revised nutrient reference values (NRVs) for labeling purposes was originally made at the November 2003 meeting of the Committee, and this year the Codex delegates were considering a discussion paper prepared by a working group under the coordination of South Africa.

NRVs can essentially be thought of as a way of describing the nutritional requirements of the average person. Naturally however this concept presents an immediate problem, because, given that each of us is genetically unique, can it really be said that there is such a thing as an "average" person? Moreover, in considering "requirements" the fundamental question then arises as to whether one is talking about the nutritional requirements for ordinary health, or those for optimum health. As always, of course, the pro-pharmaceutical lobby can easily be distinguished in these discussions by virtue of their pressing for the NRVs to be set at, or near to, RDA levels.

The setting of the NRVs at realistic levels would be an important step towards the liberation of human health and the global recognition that dietary supplements are required for the optimum functioning of the human body. No small wonder then that the pro-pharmaceutical lobby is so vigorously opposed to the NRVs being raised to levels that can only be obtained via supplementation, as the concept of optimum health is inimical to the "business with disease."

Fortunately, however, the discussion paper prepared by South Africa showed clear evidence of support for the argument that the NRVs should reflect the most recent scientific research, in order to promote optimum health and reduce the risk of disease in the majority of people. Predictably, therefore, there was a good deal of controversy over this during the meeting, and the Committee's Chairman, Dr. Rolf Grossklaus, even went so far as to interrupt South Africa during their presentation, asking them to hurry up and finish.

Later on in the discussion, in a particularly partisan intervention, Dr. Grossklaus instructed the Committee that this was not about providing consumers with optimum nutrition, but about not misleading them and setting nutrient reference values for foods for global trade purposes. Nevertheless, and as the National Health Federation (NHF) delegation then quite logically pointed out, if the mandate of the Committee was really to avoid misleading consumers then there is most definitely a need to discuss optimum nutrition levels. Significantly however, NHF was the only non-governmental delegation representing the interests of health freedom at this meeting.

Towards the end of this discussion a representative of the FAO announced that along with the World Health Organization (WHO) they were about to hold a meeting in Florence, Italy, with the goal of reaching agreement on principles and guidelines that will lead to "evidence-based dietary standards." As a part of this work FAO/WHO will apparently be discussing the possibility of setting up an expert consultation to establish new NRVs.

Clearly then, it would appear that the eventual setting of the NRVs will now be strongly influenced by FAO and WHO; two organizations with even less accountability to consumers than Codex itself.

Draft Recommendations on the Scientific Basis of Health Claims

The outcome of the Codex discussions regarding the Draft Recommendations on the Scientific Basis of Health Claims are absolutely crucial to the future of natural healthcare and health freedom, because, in order for chronic disease to become largely a thing of the past, dietary supplement manufacturers need to be able to provide truthful and non-misleading information about their products. Naturally therefore the pro-pharmaceutical lobby is becoming increasingly desperate to prevent the communication of lifesaving natural health information, as once this becomes sufficiently widespread it will essentially spell the beginning of the end for the "business with disease."

Nevertheless, and for the second year running, there was only a very limited opportunity for the Committee to consider the Recommendations at this year's meeting. Issues discussed during the short debate that did take place included authorization procedures for health claims, the scientific substantiation of health claims, and disease risk reduction claims. There was no in-depth examination of these topics however, and the Committee agreed that this work would be continued over the next year by a working group under the coordination of France.

Crucially however the European Union (EU) is currently expected to adopt a very restrictive Regulation on Nutrition and Health Claims in mid-2006. As such it seems very likely that the EU will be pushing for the Draft Recommendations on the Scientific Basis of Health Claims to be given a much higher priority at next years CCNFSDU meeting in Thailand, at which point we can expect it to begin pressing for the Recommendations to be drafted in such a way as to reflect what will then be EU law. Given the degree to which the European Union has already been able to shape the development of the Guidelines for Vitamin and Mineral Food Supplements to match its highly restrictive EU Food Supplements Directive, the extent to which it will be able to do likewise with the Recommendations on the Scientific Basis of Health Claims should not therefore be underestimated.

In this respect it is particularly worth bearing in mind the now infamous statement of the European Commission delegate at the 2003 meeting of the Committee, that health claims for vitamin and mineral supplements should be prohibited. Given that the Committee's Chairman, Dr. Rolf Grossklaus, stated at the same meeting that drugs are to mitigate and prevent diseases, and that the role of food supplements is to support the diet, the type of world that both the European Union and Codex envisage is now becoming increasingly apparent.

Discussion Paper on Risk Analysis

This discussion paper was prepared by a working group coordinated by Australia. The eventual outcome of this work has enormous relevance to the future development of the *Guidelines for Vitamin and Mineral Food Supplements,* as the *Guidelines* state that the upper safe levels of vitamins and minerals in supplements will be established by scientific risk assessment.

Notably therefore, when this agenda item was discussed at last year's meeting the Committee indicated that it would be dealing with the "over dosage of nutrients." The content of this year's discussion paper continues in much the same vein, making it abundantly clear that the Committee is intending to treat vitamins and minerals as dangerous chemicals, as opposed to essential dietary elements. Until such time as this approach changes, therefore, our health and freedoms will continue to be at risk.

The good news however is that due to a shortage of time there was very little discussion on this agenda item this year. Ominously, however, the Committee's Chairman, Dr. Rolf Grossklaus, stated that this work was of enormous importance, and that it should be given the highest priority. As such it appears likely that substantially more discussion time will be given over to this issue at next year's meeting of the Committee, in Thailand.

In addition however, it was also announced during the meeting that the final report from the FAO/WHO Nutrient Risk Assessment Project is currently being prepared, and that this should be available during or before early 2006. Moreover, the report will then be discussed at next year's meeting of the Committee. As such it seems likely that FAO/WHO will now be very influential upon not only the development of the NRVs, but also the setting of the upper safe levels for the *Guidelines for Vitamin and Mineral Food Supplements.*

The FAO/WHO Nutrient Risk Assessment Project has thus far been conducted with a disturbing lack of transparency and accountability, and, as such, the fears of many observers – that the project could eventually result in maximum levels being set for vitamin and mineral supplements that are little better than, and in some cases identical to, the RDAs – would currently appear to be entirely justified.

WHO Global Strategy on Diet, Physical Activity, and Health

The WHO Global Strategy on Diet, Physical Activity and Health [http://www.who.int/dietphysicalactivity/strategy/eb11344/strategy_english_web.pdf] was endorsed by the World Health Assembly in May 2004, and recognizes that a few largely preventable risk factors account for most of the world's disease burden. Describing how cardiovascular disease, diabetes, cancers, and obesity-related conditions now account for some 60% of global deaths and almost half (47%) of the global burden of disease, the Strategy explains how healthier diet, nutrition, and physical activity can help to prevent and control these illnesses.

At the July 2005 meeting of the Codex Alimentarius Commission, in Rome, it was decided that the potential areas for action by Codex in relation to the implementation of the Global Strategy were mainly relevant to the work of the Codex Committee on Food Labeling (CCFL) and the CCNFSDU; and that WHO, in cooperation with FAO, would produce a document for consideration by these committees, including specific proposals for new work.

Discussions on this agenda item had originally been scheduled to take place very early on in this year's CCNFSDU meeting, under agenda item 2. However, the Committee decided instead to move this debate to the very end of the last day of its meeting, and as a result there was only a very limited amount of time available to discuss the matter.

During the short discussion that did take place, WHO presented a new two-page proposal document for the Committee's consideration. Unfortunately, however, the vast majority of delegations had not even seen the document because its presence had not been previously announced and the WHO had apparently run out of copies to distribute. After a short debate therefore the Codex Secretariat stated that the Committee should report to the Codex Alimentarius Commission that there had been insufficient time to fully address the proposal, and it was decided that Codex delegations could submit comments upon the proposal to FAO/WHO by email. Nevertheless, it seemed clear that the lack of proper discussion time for this issue was totally intentional, rather than merely accidental.

Conclusion

As can be seen, the work of the CCNFSDU remains a significant danger to the future of natural healthcare and health freedom.

Specifically, the pro-pharmaceutical lobby want to see the NRVs to be set at, or near to, RDA levels, thus weakening the arguments in favour of dietary supplements; the Recommendations on the Scientific Basis of Health Claims to as far as possible prevent the communication of lifesaving information by dietary supplement manufacturers; the Discussion Paper on Risk Analysis to be developed in such a way as to ensure that the upper safe levels of vitamins and minerals are set as low as possible; and the implementation of the WHO Global Strategy on Diet, Physical Activity and Health to be delayed for as long as possible and to not interfere with the multi-trillion dollar "business with disease."

Clearly, therefore, now more than ever we must remain vigilant, as the most potentially damaging aspects of the CCNFSDU's attacks on natural healthcare and health freedom are still to come.

The end of the law is, not to abolish or restrain,
but to preserve and enlarge freedom.

- John Locke

Codex Committee in Germany Weighs Vitamin Restrictions

By Sepp Hasslberger
(Posted November 26, 2005)

The Codex Alimentarius Committee on nutrition and special dietary foods met for its yearly conclave in Bonn this week to discuss, among other things, the implementation details for its guidelines on vitamin and mineral supplements finalized a year ago and approved last July in Rome. The focus is now on the scientific evaluation of the supposed dangers of taking "too much of a good thing."

Codex is a food-related rule making body set up to facilitate international commerce. Nominally, consumer health is a primary objective, but the interests of the multinational food and pharma cartels are well represented and take precedence over nutritional health concerns. In a previous meeting, the Chairman of the Nutrition Committee Rolf Grossklaus and the representative of the EU Basil Mathioudakis famously agreed: *Nutrition has nothing to do with prevention of illness - that is the exclusive province of medicine.*

After the close of this year's meeting, the National Health Federation's delegate Scott Tips said:

> "The bad news is that these guidelines could stop millions of people around the world from using food supplements containing nutrients in sufficient amounts to benefit their health. The good news is that there is recognition by an increasing number of delegates that there are serious flaws in some of the scientific methods being used by some health authorities that are now under consideration by the

Committee. Fortunately, however, we believe its not
too late to rectify these problems."

I did not personally attend this year, but we have reports from
the National Health Federation and the Alliance for Natural
Health, two consumer-based health freedom groups concerned that
nutrition should be freely available to all, even the vitamins and
minerals contained in supplements.

The upshot: All science is not equal. Where industry - in this
case big food and big pharma – senses competition, science obligingly
bends to accommodate, even if it means treating vital nutrients as if
they were toxic chemicals.

Here is a more detailed report:
Global Vitamin Guidelines One Step Closer to Restricting Consumer Health Freedom
November 24, 2005

Today, Thanksgiving Day, sees the end of three days of meetings
of delegations from some 70 countries and numerous non-governmental organizations, at the 27th Session of the Codex Committee
on Nutrition & Foods for Special Dietary Uses (CCNFSDU) in
Bonn, Germany.

The Committee, which started developing a global guideline on
vitamin-and-mineral food supplements more than 10 years ago, was
attempting at this year's meeting to address a number of additional
contentious issues. Amongst others, these included the amounts of
vitamins and minerals required for good health, the application of
risk assessment to establish safe maximum dosages, the scientific
basis of health claims, and the implementation of the World Health
Organization's Global Strategy on Diet, Physical Activity and
Health.

The National Health Federation (NHF), a U.S.-based, international health-freedom organization of more than 50-years standing,
was the only non-governmental delegation representing the interests of vitamin consumers at this meeting.

The NHF sent three delegate members to this year's meeting.
Scott Tips, Legal Counsel for the NHF and its Codex delegation
head, said:

"The bad news is that these guidelines could stop millions of people around the world from using food supplements containing nutrients in sufficient amounts to benefit their health. The good news is that there is recognition by an increasing number of delegates that there are serious flaws in some of the scientific methods being used by some health authorities that are now under consideration by the Committee. Fortunately, however, we believe it,s not too late to rectify these problems."

Scientific Advisor to the NHF and its newest delegation member, **Dr Robert Verkerk,** who is also Executive & Scientific Director of the pan-European Alliance for Natural Health, continued:

"There is increasing scientific consensus that a sea change in the nature of the science being contemplated for both risk assessment and the setting of nutritional reference values is needed. We are working closely with scientists around the world to help facilitate this change and the NHF will be making submissions directly to the Committee's Electronic Working Groups that are dealing with these issues. If governments are going to address nutritional health seriously, they cannot any longer afford to ignore the role of high-quality food supplements in health promotion."

The NHF's Vice Chairman and veteran Codex delegate for the organization, **Paul Anthony Taylor,** added:

"Codex guidelines are, in part, supposedly designed to protect consumers, when in fact, they could actually cause harm by preventing people from accessing beneficial vitamin dosages and forms. Millions of consumers are already using dietary supplements in ways that we could not have imagined when vitamins were first discovered. For example, when the U.S. National Institutes of Health announced recently that Vitamin C selectively kills cancer cells, this information was trumpeted around the world by the media as if it were a new discovery. In reality, of course, enlightened consumers have known about this property of Vitamin C for many years now and

have been safely using this information as a means of improving their health and prolonging their lives. Codex guidelines should be assisting, not inhibiting, the spread of existing knowledge."

Unfortunately, due to a lack of time and last-minute shuffling of its schedule that relegated some of the most important issues for consumers to the end of the meeting, the Committee did not adequately discuss the agenda items on health claims and risk analysis. The NHF, along with other consumer and health-freedom groups around the world, is concerned that if excessively restrictive global guidelines for vitamins and minerals are established through Codex, consumer access to food supplements with a long history of safe use will be blocked. This would particularly be the case if countries adopt the guidelines into their own national laws, but could also occur as a result of socio-political pressures caused by the existence of internationally-recognized guidelines backed by World Trade Organization enforcement sanctions.

The NHF shall therefore continue to work with other delegations in pursuing specific and realistic pro-active strategies that will maximize consumer choice and optimize human health.

The **2006 Session of CCNFSDU** Next year's meeting in October/November will take place in Thailand. The Thai government will co-host the session along with the German Secretariat.

For further information contact:
Cheri Tips
National Health Federation
Email: ct@thenhf.com
www.thenhf.com

Shangri-La On The Rhine

The Codex Committee Meets Again in Bonn

By Scott C. Tips

(Published in *Health Freedom News*, Vol. 23, No 4, Winter 2005)

O kee," the Chairman intoned with unintended humor. Sitting at the National Health Federation's table in the meeting hall, Paul and I smiled at this fractured English. But we knew that this single word meant that German Chairman Dr. Rolf Grossklaus was satisfied that yet another item on the Codex Alimentarius Committee agenda had been covered and that the next one was up.

Paul Anthony Taylor, Dr. Robert Verkerk, and I had flown into Bonn, Germany the previous weekend in order to prepare for our attendance at the November 2005 annual meeting of the Codex Committee on Nutrition and Foods for Special Dietary Uses (CCNFSDU). Together, the three of us comprised the National Health Federation's Observer delegation at this Codex meeting, in this case the one that specifically deals with dietary-supplement guidelines. Once again, the Federation (www.thenhf.com) is the only nonprofit consumer health-freedom organization with recognized status at these Codex meetings and the concomitant ability to speak out on the issues.

This year's meeting took place during the Thanksgiving week in the same large meeting hall as before. The building, located a stone's throw away from the Rhine, held hundreds of delegates who had journeyed from around the world to brave the cold and wet German weather to attend and argue over the ten main agenda items. At times, the sun would bravely try to come out only to be invariably defeated by the dark, scudding rain clouds, which perfectly framed the Codex meeting venue.

A Different Tone This Year

Last year's meeting saw the Committee's adoption of the feared *Guidelines for Vitamin and Mineral Food Supplements*, along with the parent Codex Alimentarius Commission's perfunctory, rubber-stamp approval and adoption of those Guidelines in July 2005 despite their many failings. It is important to remember, though, that the Guidelines are nothing more than a loose framework with no teeth in them. With their adoption, the task now confronts the Committee of filling in the framework of those Guidelines with numbers and identities. What that means is that the Committee intends to set maximum upper limits for the potency of every food-supplement ingredient (the "numbers") that will appear on the not-yet-created positive list of allowable ingredients (the "identities"). Therein lies the challenge.

In the past, the meetings have been rancorous and contentious, particularly between the NHF and South Africa, on the one side, and the European Commission (EC) and its European and pharma-ceutical allies on the other. With the Guidelines adopted, howev-er, the tone has changed to one where there is less drama as the bat-tles are being fought on the fringes. In other words, the Committee is delegating the "framework filling" tasks to working groups with-in the Committee, which working groups report back to the Committee every year on their progress. The NHF is a member of each of these working groups.

Nutrient Reference Values

Nutrient Reference Values ("NRVs") are nothing more than souped-up RDAs. These are numerical values assigned to each nutrient so as to reflect the mythical average person's nutritional needs for that nutrient. By referring to the NRV for, say, calcium, the consumer is supposed to get an idea of whether he or she is get-ting an adequate (or in European bureaucratic eyes, an excessive) amount of calcium. These values are supposed to be set according to rigorous scientific evidence; but, as I have long contended, "science" at Codex levels is far more political than scientific. NRVs will be established politically.

Dr. Grossklaus, the Chairman of CCNSFDU, is a prime example of this lack of objectivity. We all know that a good committee chairman will conduct a meeting fairly. Yet, remember that Dr. Grossklaus is also a member of the German Risk Assessment Institute (BfR) that recently came out with its report proposing Maximum Permitted Levels for vitamins and minerals at absurdly low levels (e.g., the maximum potencies for Vitamin C and niacin would be 225 mgs and 17 mgs, respectively). Thus, he already has set in his mind where this game should go and it was clearly reflected in his comments to South Africa.

Last year, South Africa had graciously accepted the burden of preparing for the Committee a discussion paper on the fundamental principles that should govern NRVs. At this year's meeting, South African delegate head Antoinette Booyzen presented the discussion paper to the Committee only to be interrupted six minutes into her presentation by the Chairman's very curt remarks telling her to hurry up. Unrattled, Ms. Booyzen continued with her presentation. Because South Africa's paper dared to mention that NRVs should take into account the optimal nutritional needs of consumers, South Africa was criticized again by the Chairman for a lack of objectivity and jumped on by several delegations, including the United States and the EC. In particular, Dr. Grossklaus said that optimal nutrition would be misleading to consumers. On behalf of the NHF, I spoke up in defense of South Africa, disagreeing with the Chairman and replying that it would mislead consumers **not** to take into account optimal nutrition because otherwise consumers would be misled into thinking that they were getting adequate amounts of nutrients when in fact they were not.

Notwithstanding his displeasure, the Chairman extended South Africa's mandate to manage this task. South Africa will take into account the additional input of other delegations, revise its presentation paper, and re-present it at the 2006 CCNFSDU meeting.

Parenthetically, the delegates were told that a Food and Agriculture Organization (FAO) and the World Health Organization (WHO) would meet in December 2005 in Florence, Italy for the purpose of agreeing on principles and guidelines that will result in "evidence-based" dietary standards. There, the FAO and WHO plan to formulate some manner of expert-consultation group that would establish FAO/WHO proposed NRVs.

Health Claims

"Okee," we heard again as the Chairman moved on to this agenda item concerning health claims for food supplements. Because so much time had been spent on dietary-fiber and infant-formula standards, though, there was extremely little time devoted to this topic. Of course, the EC view has been that health claims for food supplements should be prohibited – period. Many delegations agree with this viewpoint, but there is enough opposition to a flat prohibition to perhaps avoid achieving consensus on this point. Regardless, the general American health consumer's view of liberality for such claims – not espoused by the U.S. delegation by the way – will never be adopted in this atmosphere of governmental paternalism.

As with the NRVs, food-supplement health claims are the province of a working group – this one chaired by France. The French delegate head presented her report to the Committee. But, curiously, even though she took as long to present her report as did Ms. Booyzen, Dr. Grossklaus refrained from interrupting her to tell her to hurry up and finish – probably because time works differently in the Northern Hemisphere. France's mandate to continue with its work here was also continued by the Committee.

Although there was some discussion about substantiating health claims and even permitting disease-reduction health claims, the problem that we face here is that most of the Codex countries themselves have made any dietary-supplement health claims illegal or so nominal as to be useless. And the existing draft Recommendations for Health Claims reflects this view. Unfortunately, in their blind haste to protect consumers from themselves, the regulators are actually consigning consumers to an informational black hole in which they will be kept ignorant of truthful dietary information important to their health.

Risk Analysis

"Okee." We moved on to the agenda item dealing with risk analysis (which is composed of three elements: risk assessment, risk management, and risk communication). Also the object of a working group, this topic is being managed by the delegation of Australia. Ms. Janine Lewis, the Australian delegation head, presented her report on the application of risk analysis to the work of the

Committee. Despite the extremely short amount of time available to discuss risk-analysis issues, the Chairman did not interrupt Ms. Lewis either. Dr. Grossklaus did, however, praise her report and said that her working group's efforts were of "enormous importance."

I'll say. It is risk analysis and its offspring, risk assessment, that will be used to set the safe upper limits for vitamins and minerals within the Codex framework. If those limits are set high, then we will all have more breathing room. If, however, they are set low, then we will be in deep trouble.

Thanks to Dr. Robert Verkerk, NHF's science advisor and also director of the Alliance for Natural Health, who analyzed the Australian discussion paper and prepared a point-by-point response, the NHF submitted to the Committee and working group this response. At the heart of this response was the fact that natural substances such as vitamins and minerals should not be treated in the same way as toxic substances and that the methodologies applied should take that factor into account as well as the particular forms of the vitamins and minerals and their amounts.

As with the other two working groups, Australia's mandate was continued and Ms. Lewis stated that it would take more years before the risk-analysis standards could be established and applied.

Side Notes About the Meeting

Interesting enough, at the beginning of the meeting, Dr. Grossklaus announced that the CCNFSDU must improve its public image and he requested permission of the Committee to allow it to be videotaped for a promotional film. When he said this, I could only think that Kevin Miller's anti-Codex documentary, *We Become Silent: The Last Days of Health Freedom*, must be having enough of an impact for the Chairman and his handlers to be worried. So, throughout the meeting, a camera crew scurried around with its equipment taking various shots of delegates speaking and the Chairman pontificating.

The NHF delegation also noticed that the developing nations in attendance at the meeting were significantly more vocal this year than ever before. Tanzania and Ghana were especially bold at putting forth their positions and then firmly standing their ground, even in the face of opposition. It was a refreshing sight.

Although generally known during the meeting, at the end it

was formally announced that the 2006 CCNSFDU meeting would be held in Chiangmai, Thailand from October 30th through November 3rd. Then, the meeting adjourned. Okee?

Part III

(2006-Present)

Codex Committee
for Food Labeling

By Scott C. Tips
Ottawa, Canada (May 1-5, 2006)

(Published in *Health Freedom News*, Vol. 24, No. 2, Summer 2006)

A t the 34th Session of the Codex Committee on Food Labeling (CCFL), held in Ottawa, Canada from May 1-5, 2006, the CCFL met in order to discuss several issues of importance to consumers. Among other things, the CCFL discusses and proposes guidelines on food labeling, food definitions, advertising, and any matters referred to it by the Codex Alimentarius Commission (CAC), the Food and Agriculture Organization (FAO), and/or the World Health Organization (WHO).

The National Health Federation, the only consumer health-freedom group with accreditation to attend and speak out at such Codex meetings, was present throughout the entire meeting and its working groups in order to monitor the Committee's work and to provide a voice at the meeting for those consumers who wish to preserve their health choices through a free flow of information from all sources.

The Global Strategy

The first day of the meeting opened early on with a presentation by Janice Albert, the representative of the FAO, discussing the WHO's "Global Strategy on Diet, Physical Activity, and Health," in which she made several main points about the Global Strategy: (1)

that its aim was to prevent and control "the heavy and growing burden of non-communicable diseases"; and (2) that the FAO endorsed this Strategy. Further areas for developing the Strategy, she added, would be: (1) promoting labeling to allow consumers to be better informed about the benefits and contents of foods; (2) adopting measures to minimize the impact of marketing on unhealthy dietary patterns; (3) providing more information about healthy consumption patterns; and (4) adopting production and processing standards regarding the nutritional quality and safety of products. Importantly, during her presentation, not once did Ms. Albert mention food supplements.[1]

Nor did any of the other delegations discussing this topic mention food supplements as a critical element for optimizing health and nutrition, until South Africa spoke. The South African delegate, Antoinette Booyzen, proposed the inclusion within the Global Strategy of a comprehensive list of 11 health-optimizing points, including, among other things, recognizing that nutrients were not toxins and should be generally recognized as safe, allowing the enrichment of foods with dietary supplements so as to optimize nutrient density, and supporting nutrition and health claims and advertising for those foods that contribute to a healthy lifestyle while banning such claims that do not. The NHF was the only other delegation present that spoke up in support of the South African proposal, although it could be argued that the Senegalese delegate's preceding remarks indirectly supported South Africa. Without broad support, the South African proposal was not accepted for inclusion.

After a break, the CCFL Chairwoman, Dr. Anne MacKenzie, announced that the Committee should approve 5 main themes involving the Global Strategy, which themes were drafted by unnamed parties during the break. Those themes were: (1) Enhancing and improving the label information about the nutritional aspects of food to assist consumers in making informed health choices about foods; (2) The importance of truthful and non-misleading marketing practices and advertising in promoting the nutritional aspects of foods; (3) Codex standards should not impede the development of modified versions of foods intended to improve consumers' food choices [read: GMOs should not be forbidden]; (4) The importance of sound science in implementing the Global Strategy; and (5) Improving access to information that is adequate, accurate, and truthful. The Chairwoman then asked for comments from the delegates.

The NHF pointed out to the Committee that it was easy for us delegates to nit-pick the work done by others and that the Chairwoman should be commended for the 5 Themes, which covered the two general topics of health protection and truthful information. However, the NHF added that those two topics are just subsets of our overriding goal here of ensuring that people will be healthier, and that unfortunately nowhere in the 5 Themes was there any mention of "optimizing health and nutrition." The NHF therefore proposed, and the Chairwoman accepted, that the phrase "The role of adequate information that is truthful must be taken into consideration" have the words "and that optimizes health and nutrition" inserted after "truthful" so as to reflect this broader theme. It looked like a victory for health freedom!

At that point, though, the delegate from the United States, Barbara Schneeman, asked to be recognized and then said that the United States opposed the inclusion of those words because it would not be good to tinker with the wording of the themes. The Chairwoman then promptly deleted the NHF's previously-accepted wording from the text, since, under Codex procedural rules, a country's stated position will prevail over that of a nongovernmental organization such as the NHF.[2] Thanks, then, to the United States and the United States alone there is no mention of optimizing health and nutrition in the 5 Themes of the Global Strategy.

The Chairwoman then announced that the FAO and WHO would prepare a document that would take into account the 5 Themes, which would then be presented at the next meeting of the Codex Committee on Nutrition and Foods for Special Dietary Uses in November 2006. CCFL would then revisit the enhanced report at its next meeting.

GMO Labeling

The next hot topic at the CCFL meeting centered around genetically modified organisms and whether or not they needed to be fully disclosed on food labels. Contrary to most of the rest of the World, the general position of the food-exporting Western Hemispheric delegations (Canada, USA, Mexico, and Argentina) was that GMO labeling was not a topic that the Committee should take up and that it should be dropped from the agenda. The NHF disagreed with that position and supported full disclosure of GMO ingredients on food labels so that consumers may make fully-informed health choices.

Since no consensus was reached on this topic, the Chairwoman accepted Norway's suggestion for a physical working group to meet in Norway next January 2007, and the NHF added its name to the many other delegations which will be in attendance there.

Trans-Fatty Acid and Advertising Definitions

Two issues that the Committee was charged with considering were the definitions of trans-fatty acids[3] and advertising.[4] In both cases, there was broad disagreement and, so, no consensus was reached after considerable discussion.

Importantly, as the disagreement over the definition of trans-fatty acids raged on, the Chairwoman noted that "We are all aware of sovereign rights, so there is nothing to prevent the member countries from revising [the definition] as they will." This comment was in line with her earlier comments that the CCFL guidelines were just "indicative" and not required, words that are important to many of us who see Codex Guidelines as the harbinger of national things to come.

In its opposition to the definition of trans-fatty acids, South Africa noted the definition as proposed would cover certain naturally-occurring substances, such as conjugated linoleic acid (CLA), which could result in them being unfairly and incorrectly branded as health hazards.

In turn, the NHF opposed the Canadian-proposed definition of advertising because it could result in the prohibition of advertising legitimate, published, peer-reviewed research papers, among other things. The United States delegation, supported by several other delegations, expressed the opinion that it was not appropriate for the Committee to define advertising, which definition best be left to national authorities.

Overview

Well-run,[5] the CCFL meeting progressed steadily despite strong disagreements among the country delegations. The main areas of friction were about the WHO Global Strategy themes, mandatory GMO labeling, and – interestingly enough – the definitions of trans-fatty acids and advertising. All of these issues were referred on for further discussion and work, but there was never any consensus or agreement that health and nutrition must be optimized or that dietary supplements have a role to play in optimizing health and nutrition, although the National Health Federation came extremely close to inserting important language to that effect in the Global Strategy's themes. Unfortunately, the United States – represented here as it always is by an FDA functionary – saw to it that such important language was eliminated from the Global Strategy.

Clearly, with anti-health-freedom delegations such as the United States and the European Commission running the show at Codex and with most other delegations blissfully uncaring or unknowledge-able about the true health benefits that optimal health and nutrition play in preventing disease and other health problems, the direction of the various Codex guidelines is still off-course.

---

[1] In fact, in a private conversation NHF held with Ms. Albert the following day, she said that at the last CAC meeting in Rome (July 2005) there had been no condemnation by FAO or WHO of Codex on the subject of nutrition and that, while she agreed that natural sub-stances should not be treated in the same manner as toxins, natural substances such as food supplements must be checked and controlled also.

[2] At the very next break, the NHF delegate angrily demanded of Dr. Schneeman why she had asked for the removal of the "optimizes health and nutrition" wording. Taken aback, she claimed that we must look at the broader picture, that we could not allow the themes to be tinkered with, and that such wording might imply that labeling would have to have such information. The NHF said, if anything, her position showed that the FDA opposes optimizing health and nutrition!

[3] Defined as "all the geometrical isomers of monounsaturated and polyunsaturated fatty acids having non-conjugated, interrupted by at least one methylene group, carbon-carbon double bonds in the trans configuration."

[4] Defined as "any representation to the public, by any means other than a label, that is intended or is likely to influence and shape attitude, beliefs and behaviors in order to pro-mote directly or indirectly the sale of any food."

[5] Whatever may be said of the direction of Codex, it must be stated that Chairwoman Anne MacKenzie was competent, astute, and extremely knowledgeable in her handling of the meeting as its chairwoman, only once failing to recognize the NHF to speak (and that due to obvious time constraints) - all qualities to be appreciated.

"The greatest dangers to liberty lurk in insidious encroachment by men of zeal, well-meaning but without understanding.

- U.S. Supreme Court Justice Louis D. Brandeis
in Whitney v. California (1927)

Report from the Thai Codex Meeting

By Ingrid Franzon

Head of the NHF delegation to the 28th CCNFSDU
Codex meeting in Chiang Mai, Thailand

(Published in *Health Freedom News*, Vol. 24, No. 4, Winter 2006)

The best way to describe the 28th Codex Committee on Nutrition and Foods for Special Dietary Uses (CCNFSDU) meeting is as a national and geographic polarization. Most delegations are made up of government officials and interested parties – in other words the industry affected by the laws on food, health claims, and labeling being discussed. The health interests of the consumer do not come first and this is why the attendance and interventions from the International Non-Governmental Organizations (INGOs) is so important.

In particular, the National Health Federation was there in order to monitor this meeting and to provide an alternative viewpoint on food-standard issues – such as risk assessment – that would otherwise be sorely missing. It was a new challenge for me to head the NHF delegation to this year's meeting and I was ably supported by NHF's science advisor Dr. Robert Verkerk from the United Kingdom and NHF member Dr. Wong Ang Peng from Malaysia. The three of us initiated heated discussions at the meeting that illuminated the need for Codex standards to better consider consumers' metabolic, national, and geographic differences. As always, the NHF delegation definitely stands out from the crowd.

Codex Meetings

Codex Alimentarius comes under the direction of two United Nations organs: the Food and Agriculture Organization (FAO) and the World Health Organization (WHO). The tasks assigned to Codex are in turn carried out by various committees such as the CCNFSDU, which are assigned to work out compromise solutions on issues on food, ones that all countries can live with. That is the intention; but it is not an easy task considering the geographic location, lifestyle, and diet of the World's participating countries. Decisions are made at Steps from 1 to 8, where Step 8 signifies finalization. After ratification by the Codex Commission, the proposition has to be implemented in import and export laws in all member states. In time, this will also come to affect national products.

Discussions with other INGOs present were enlightening. Some INGOs think that the decisions made will not concern their country. In other words, they believe that they can participate in forming Codex policy for the rest of the world, but be exempt from enforcing it in their own. Imagine what that would be like, a country that chooses not to implement Codex will no longer be able to import or export from other Codex countries. Surely this will in turn also affect everything produced in this country in the end – if this country is not to be totally isolated?

Those of us who believe in health freedom in the industrialized world tend to see Codex as a restrictive body. It was interesting to see some of the upsides of Codex in discovering how small industries in Thailand have been enabled by Codex. But the biggest question in my mind is whether or not Codex enables growth and development while at the same time imposing the industrial world's restrictive "benefits" on the rest of the World – and all the while making sure that national and industrial interests in the developed countries are prioritized.

Agenda Items of Interest

This particular Codex meeting offered several agenda items of interest: the World Health Organization's Global Strategy on Diet, Physical Activity and Health, nutrient risk assessment, health claims, and Nutrient Reference Values (NRVs), the last of which currently seems the most likely candidate to replace Recommended Daily Allowances (RDAs) for vitamins and minerals.

The NHF has also been taking an active part in the Working Group on risk assessment, a discipline that is being earmarked to become the key scientific justification for potential future bans on dietary supplements. Current risk-assessment methods are flawed and biased, so methodologies that are scientifically rational are urgently required and were central to the NHF's interventions in the discussions held during this year's meeting.

The Infant Formula Problem

One of the more interesting discussions that took place during the committee meetings had to do with fatty acids in infant formula for special needs. The Japanese delegate questioned why the proposed levels of arachidonic acid in infant formula were set to be no less than the levels of DHA. He pointed out that there is exceedingly little arachidonic acid in the breast milk of Japanese mothers and opposed the addition of arachidonic acid in the formula as the proposed formula would force Japanese children to consume levels of arachidonic acid that are foreign to their race and culture.

The U.S. delegation claimed that American research shows that the levels of DHA and AA should be the same. One can also wonder if the high levels of arachidonic acid in the breast milk of mothers from industrialized countries could be as a result of their diet. After considerable discussion, the CCNFSDU Chairman Dr. Grossklaus finally came to the conclusion that the committee had reached a consensus and decided in favor of DHA and AA remaining at the same level. Although the microphone was turned off, the whole assembly could hear the voice of the Japanese delegate shouting "No, no, no, no!"

At this point the Chairman made an unprecedented decision. He ruled that Japan (read, any country) should be allowed to follow its national custom and not be forced to use the internationally-produced infant formula. Even this is prohibitive for some nationalities; and as the African delegate from Benin pointed out, Japan may be able to make its own infant formula, but Benin is at the mercy of the producers. Benin expressed deep concern that the nutrients in infant formula should be as similar to real breast milk as possible.

The Japanese delegate was still broken at the coffee break that followed. Shaking his head, he said, "I don't understand why they don't listen to me!" This, almost as much as anything, was a sad example revealing the real backside of Codex. The countries with the strongest industrial and political power tend to get their voices heard, and at this particular meeting these were the United States and the European Union (EU). Decision by consensus is dependant upon voices being raised and opinions being heard. Language, culture, and understanding of the issues are dependant on so many things.

Despite the negative aspects of this discourse, this was in fact an unprecedented event for one particular aspect of health freedom! It was now the second time during the Codex meeting in Chiang Mai that we saw a move to accept an individual interpretation or ruling. Earlier in the meeting it was generally stated that if a child could tolerate the formula at the recommended dose, then the Guidance Upper Limits (GULs) would not have to be adhered to. In other words, any child who can consume the formula without ill-effect can therefore drink as much of the formula as the child (or mother) wishes without regard to whether the GULs have been exceeded. For Codex, this was a brave act indeed.

In fact, even more, the Committee did on the other hand succeed in establishing – perhaps unwittingly – a concept important to health freedom. NHF pointed this out, and for the record it is stated in the Codex Report at paragraph 28 that, "With reference to the question of upper levels, the Observer from NHF supported the principle that 'when children have already adapted well to the formula, there is no need to follow the upper limit' and proposed that it should be applied to food supplements for all age groups."

The Chairman Misallocates Time

This infant-formula item finished at a Step 8, but blocked several other important issues from being addressed, that some delegations had traveled halfway round the World to take part in. Because the CCNFSDU discussions on infant formula and foods occupied some 75% of the Committee's time and energy, certain critical agenda items concerning health claims, NRVs, and risk assessment ended up getting the short end of the stick – only one-and-a-half hours the evening of the final session and even then only because the meeting was extended!

Was this marginalization intentional? Some have speculated that the continued low priority for these agenda items over successive CCNFSDU meetings is perhaps being orchestrated by Codex in order to allow the European Commission to make more progress in finalizing its own regulations in these areas. Once the Commission's own regulations are completed, it is said, they would then serve as the model for future Codex standards. NHF and other delegations are considering handing in a formal complaint about the lack of chairmanship that leads to this marginalization year after year.

Nevertheless, despite the marginalization of key agenda items, the NHF considers the earlier discussion on infant formulas to have generated an unexpected and important precedent – one that also affects future laws on food supplements. The EU and Codex are attempting to create rigid, "one size fits all" international guidelines for food-supplement ingredients, while the NHF believes that this approach fundamentally goes against individual and national rights and needs on the grounds of geographic, genetic, and metabolic differences. We shall see which view prevails.

When you drink the water, remember the spring.
- Chinese proverb

When it Comes to GM Food, Some Say Ignorance is Bliss

By Tamara Thérèsa Mosegaard,
Head of the NHF delegation, and Scott C. Tips
(Published in *Health Freedom News*, Vol 25, No 1, Spring 2007)

At a recent two-day meeting in Oslo, Norway, a sizeable group of delegates met to discuss establishing international Codex Guidelines for disclosing genetically-modified (GM) ingredients on food-product labels. Amazingly enough, several important countries' delegates argued that consumers were not smart enough to understand and handle such information. Ignorance is bliss, they essentially claimed.

The National Health Federation, the only health-freedom organization with the right to attend and have its voice heard at these meetings, sent its own two-person delegation – Ingrid Franzon and me – to argue for the right of all persons to know what they are consuming, especially if it is GM food. In doing so, the NHF verbally sparred with such countries as the United States, Argentina, Canada, and Mexico (the largest grain-exporting countries), all of whom took the carefully coordinated position that consumers should not be informed as to whether they are eating GM foods or not.

Other countries, generally called the Grain Importers, such as the 27 European nation-states (the EU, including Austria, France, Germany, Ireland, Italy, and Sweden), Brazil, Ghana, India, Japan, Morocco, Norway and Switzerland, strongly opposed hiding such information from the consumer. The result was at times high melodrama employing plans obviously orchestrated by the Grain Exporters, who variously used polite anger, polite aggression, as well as manipulative language and tactics (with everyone else understanding that they might end the meetings through their non-participation) in an attempt to stop any progress towards Codex Guidelines that would require GM disclosure.

The Meeting Begins

It all began amicably enough with the Norwegian "FDA," called "Mattilsynet," hosting a two-day Codex Alimentarius Working Group meeting on the subject of the "Labeling of Foods and Food Ingredients Obtained through Certain Techniques of Genetic Modification/Genetic Engineering." The Norwegians were gracious hosts with the meeting taking place at the Bristol Hotel in Oslo, Norway on the two very cold days of February 6th and 7th, 2007. Besides the NHF, there were 24 national delegations and four other international non-governmental organizations (INGOs) present, plus a scattering of individual observers, staff members, and interpreters, some 77 individuals in all. For those unfamiliar with Codex "Working Groups," these are usually specially-focused collections of delegates interested in particular topics covered by a particular Codex Alimentarius committee, in this case the Codex Committee on Food Labeling (CCFL) that meets every year in Canada to discuss and advance Labeling guidelines.

Norway, Argentina, and Ghana acted jointly as chairmen of the meeting, which opened with a proposal that a table of the various Labeling approaches be discussed and developed. Soon enough, a large rift between the Grain Exporters and the Grain Importers became evident, as the Grain Exporters expounded their views that because consumers were different from each other, they did not all need much information about the production methods of GM foods, and if it were given to them, then it could be deemed a "warning" and therefore misleading and damaging to them and – perhaps most importantly – the GM industry.

The Grain Importers Think GM
Foods Are Safe But Want Them Labeled

The Grain Importers strongly believed that their scientific risk-assessment procedures were adequate enough to ensure that GM foods were safe when they reached consumers' tables, but they equally strongly recognized the importance of consumer information

.hrough proper Labeling of GM food products.

Yet, we found it was strange to hear the European Community EC] talk about scientific risk assessment proving the safety of GM oods, and the need for consumers to be well informed, when I emember the many years of discussions at the Codex Alimentarius Committee meetings about establishing 'upper safe (maximum) levels of vitamins and minerals through scientific risk (safety) assessment based upon scientific data.' Strange, when in the EC many health products are now registered as pharmaceuticals and are either waiting to be tested by very costly procedures because of 'risk assessment,' or have already been banned. So, in essence, we – the consumers – have been told that vitamins and minerals can be dangerous to our sensitive health but that we will only stay healthy by eating a balanced, GM functional-food diet. Maybe some people believe this, but most consumers are not that ignorant.

Because of this, natural health, health freedom, and freedom of information and choice have become huge issues, especially in Europe, with more than 70% of the consumers in several countries saying no to GM food, and a majority wanting mandatory Labeling so that at least they will know what they are buying and eating.

At the meeting, this view was clearly supported by the majority of attendees. But the primarily Western Hemispheric countries that export GM grains and other foods to the rest of the World were obviously concerned about consumer acceptance of GM foods. These countries know that, as I stated at the meeting on behalf of NHF, most consumers – given a choice – will reject GM foods in favor of non-GM foods that have been grown, harvested, and consumed over many centuries, if not millennia. Indeed, among other studies, a very recently-released (but previously suppressed) 1998 Russian study suggests that such suspicion is well warranted since these researchers at the Institute of Nutrition at the Russian Academy of Medical Sciences had found that GM potatoes containing an antibiotic resistance marker caused significant damage to test rats' internal organs.

The Grain Exporting Empire Strikes Back

So it was that in remarkably well-coordinated maneuvering, the U.S., Canadian, and Argentinean delegates argued about how they doubted the value of consumer information, how they wanted to prevent "fraud and deception," and how it was important first to see how the consumers were using the GM Labeling information as the labels might be seen as a warning, which would be misleading. Compare these viewpoints with the many years of disproportionate misinformation disseminated through media warnings and these countries' own regulatory agencies about the "dangers" of vitamins and minerals, which are in turn fueling and leading to unnecessary national and global Codex restrictions upon natural and healthy substances.

The U.S. representative, Dr. Barbara Schneeman of the U.S. Food and Drug Administration, was especially pointed and heated in her discussions. Amazingly enough, in an unconstitutional flight of fancy, she claimed that "they" (the FDA and government) *should only give consumers the information that the government thought they would understand.*

And later, in conversation with other delegates outside the meeting, Dr. Schneeman – quite upset that there was sustained opposition to the Grain Exporters' position that consumers would be "confused" if they saw products Labeled as "GM" on store shelves – claimed incredibly enough that the First Amendment prevents the government from mandating label information telling consumers about the GM content or origin of their food products!

Yet, as most readers will recall, the First Amendment to the United States Constitution states quite plainly that *"Congress shall make no law respecting an establishment of religion, or prohibiting the free exercise thereof; or abridging the freedom of speech, or of the press; or the right of the people peaceably to assemble, and to petition the government for a redress of grievances."*

The United States Supreme Court, as well as a number of lesser American courts, has long held in numerous rulings that the First Amendment is not, and never was, intended to suppress free speech but rather to encourage its free exercise. Regardless, the FDA itself has never been shy when it comes to asserting control over food-product label content in the United States – in fact the Agency does it routinely. So, why is it now curiously taking the position that American law prevents it from doing so in the case of GM foods? Perhaps the GM food producers – such as Monsanto – that were also represented at this meeting and that were practically sitting on Dr. Schneeman's lap might have had something to do with this aberrant change.

Risk Prevention Not an Issue Here

Also strangely enough, for the Grain Exporters in this Working Group, risk prevention did not seem to be an issue at all. The Argentinean delegation implied that it would be unethical to refuse GM foods to consumers. And all of the Grain Exporters strongly argued the cost effectiveness – to the GM industry of course – of GM food products, not a huge surprise considering how much money is at stake with this technology, based upon highly-persistent and toxic pesticides as well as patents on 'terminator' technology (which genetically can switch off a plant's ability to further germinate and would require chemicals to switch it back on).

Most delegates did not see GM technology as threatening irreversible harm to consumers because, as a Grain Exporter delegation stated, "the technology has had 10-15 years of use without any problems." Yet, as with the deleterious effects of many pharmaceutical drugs, which do not appear for some decades after their initial use, the heated debate on safety issues concerning GM foods is far from over.

The NHF and Others Argue Back

In remembering the famous quote by the American Chief Judge at the Nuremberg War-Crimes Tribunal, Robert H. Jackson (who said "It is not the function of our Government to keep the citizen from falling into error; it is the function of the citizen to keep the Government from falling into error"), I told the Working Group's attendees that NHF was present because consumers are concerned about their freedom of choice through lack of information.

And, more specifically, when it came time for a response to Argentina, Canada, and Mexico's arguments that there are many different types of consumers, not all of whom were concerned about GM foods, I said that "We are all consumers, but we are here to represent concerned consumers-citizens. There are different views and concerns. Argentina brought up ethical and religious reasons, there are also health, safety, information, and freedom-of-choice concerns."

At the end, the Federation supported the pro-consumer information views expressed by Morocco, Japan, the EC, and even the nonprofit organization Consumers International (with whom NHF had been at odds over the dietary-supplement issue), adding further that it "supports full disclosure of GM ingredients on food labels so that consumers may make fully-informed health choices, and therefore is in favor of mandatory Labeling. We are in favor of information and transparency, which is extraordinarily needed in this area because of its highly technological nature and its possible and probable effect on the future of mankind. Studies have shown that there are reasons to be concerned."

The meeting ended on a high note for most of the delegates with a mandate to continue its work on GM Labeling, much to the dislike of the Grain Exporter delegations which would rather have seen this issue discarded so that GM food products could be sold in anonymity along with non-GM products, with consumers blissfully ignorant of the difference.

Still, this meeting's importance primarily lay in serving as a microcosm-forum for this worldwide debate about GM foods. In just two days, the views and arguments expressed by the two opposed sides were clearly stated and noted. Yet while those forces suspicious of or outright opposed to GM foods prevailed at this meeting, as Winston Churchill once said, "Success is never final." Regardless, at this stage, consumers have made it crystal clear that they would rather eat non-GM foods and that, in order to do so, GM foods must be identified as such.

North American Union:

FDA's Trilateral Cooperation Charter With Canada & Mexico
Threatens to Scuttle Consumer Access to Dietary Supplements

By John C. Hammell

In 1991, in Baden-Baden, Germany, David Rockefeller gloatingly said: "We're grateful to The Washington Post, The New York Times, Time Magazine and other great publications whose directors have attended our meetings and respected their promises of discretion *for almost forty years*. **It would have been impossible for us to develop our plan for the world if we had been subject to the bright lights of publicity during those years. But the world is now more sophisticated and *prepared to march towards a world government..*"** (emphasis added)[1]

High treason has been committed against the United States by a succession of Presidents, Senators, and Congressmen whose loyalty has not been to the Constitution, but to the ruling elite's long-held plan to destroy the sovereignty of nations and to force the people of the World into a global totalitarian state. Many of these Presidents and members of Congress are members of the Bilderbergers, Trilateral Commission, and the Council on Foreign Relations (CFR).

The Trojan Horse

On March 23, 2005, President Fox, Prime Minister Martin, and President Bush used the North American Free Trade Agreement (NAFTA) as a Trojan horse to create the Security and Prosperity Partnership of North America (SPP). The FDA's Trilateral Cooperation Charter with Canada and Mexico was created under the auspices of NAFTA and the SPP.

NAFTA, a supposed "trade agreement" that has already cost millions of American jobs and closed many of our manufacturing plants, has been deviously used to create the SPP. It was an ignominious day for America and all she stands for when the heads of state from three sovereign countries (Mexico, Canada, and America) could simply **mutually agree** to deviously pervert the NAFTA agreement and create the SPP. [34] [5]

Having made their official announcement, President Bush believed he was then entitled to order the executive branch of our government to do his bidding to create the North American Union (NAU) under cover of the SPP without any oversight by Congress or informing the American public.

Ergo, **by presidential fiat,** Bush has created **"an end run around America's sovereignty, eroding it piece by piece"** or, rather, "department by department" just as announced by CFR member Richard Gardner in his 1974 *Foreign Affairs* article.

At the same time, we have received what Miguel Pickard has characterized as **an** "Early Warning Wake-up Call" from Mexico:

"Their ideas are being implemented *through the signing of "regulations" not subject to citizens' review.* This vision may initially have been labeled NAFTA Plus, but the name gives a mistaken impression of what is at hand, since there will be no single treaty text, no unique label to facilitate keeping tabs. Perhaps for this reason, some civil society groups are calling the phenomenon by another name, the Security and Prosperity Partnership of North America (SPPNA), an official sobriquet for the summits held by the three chief executives to agree on the future of "North America". . . . This explains in part why *deeper integration is taking place through a series of regulations and executive decrees that avoid citizen watchdogs and legislative oversight.* Activist civil society organizations have to work overtime to keep up." (emphasis added)[6]

Working Overtime
The International Advocates for Health Freedom (IAHF) is currently working overtime and getting nowhere in an effort to expose and stop FDA's Trilateral Cooperation Charter and the

North American Union dictatorship. In July 2006, I filed a Freedom of Information Act (FOIA) request with the FDA in order to procure all internal documents pertaining to their **Trilateral Cooperation Charter** with Canada and Mexico.[7]

I filed this FOIA request because it is apparent to me that the FDA is attempting to make an end run around the Dietary Supplement Health and Education Act of 1994 (DSHEA) by liaising with regulatory counterparts from Canada and Mexico, countries that have much more restrictive regulatory regimes for dietary supplements than America has. (In Canada and Mexico, dietary supplements are regulated as "drugs," and access is far more restricted than it is in the USA where they are regulated as foods under the Dietary Supplement Health and Education Act of 1994.)[8][9]

Despite two conference calls with Naomi Kawin, the U.S. Country Coordinator for the Trilateral Cooperation Charter, Associate Director for the Americas, Office of International Programs, Office of the Commissioner, the FDA has not sent me any of their internal documents as of April 1, 2007.

The FDA has lied to me three times now about when they would get documents to me per my FOIA request. First, they said that I would get my documents "before the end of the year [2006]." Then, they said "by the end of January," then "by the end of February." Naomi Kawin has failed to return my last several emails and phone calls and it is obvious to me that the FDA won't give up these documents unless and until someone takes them to Federal District Court.

FDA Is Subverting American Law

Look at FDA's overly broad definition of "fraud" as found within the Trilateral Cooperation Charter, which can be found at *http://www.fda.gov/oia/charter.html* (see "Appendix B"). Its definition of Health Fraud is as follows:

"For the purposes of this Working Group, health fraud may include the following: The false, deceptive, or misleading promotion, advertisement, distribution, sale, possession for sale, or offering for sale of products or provision of services, intended for human use, that are represented as being safe and/or effective to diagnose, prevent, cure, treat, or mitigate disease (or other conditions), to rehabilitate patients or to <u>provide a beneficial effect on health</u>."

(emphasis added) (Under this definition, FDA can ban any dietary supplement currently on the market in the USA, they could ban *water* under this definition.)

The FDA is clearly trying to make an end run around DSHEA.[10] The FDA *hates* this law! They *hate* it because it was passed in the direct face of an FDA-rulemaking effort in 1992 called the Dykstra Report.[11]

What they are clearly attempting to do via the Trilateral Cooperation Charter is to roll things back to the way they would have been if DSHEA had not effectively countered the Dykstra Report in 1994.

The Dykstra Report was an Advance Notice of Proposed Rulemaking generated by the FDA to announce intended regulations which would accompany passage of the Nutrition Labeling and Education Act of 1990 (NLEA). NLEA was a direct attack on the dietary-supplement industry, an effort to repeal the Proxmire Amendment of 1976, which blocked a previous FDA initiative that would have banned consumer access to vitamins and minerals within the therapeutic range.

The Dykstra Report: A Landmark Attack

"*On June 18, 1993, the FDA published an Advanced Notice of Proposed Rulemaking (ANPR) concerning the regulation of dietary supplements. This document referred to a number of factors that had led the FDA to revise dietary supplement regulations. These factors included increased consumer use of dietary supplements, an internal FDA three-year review of possible new regulatory approaches, the occurrence of eosinophilia myalgia syndrome from a contaminated batch of l-tryptophan, and (alleged) reports of serious illnesses from the use of botanical supplements.*

The ANPR also was called the Dykstra Report, after its author, Gary Dykstra of the FDA. It proposed that free access to vitamins and minerals be limited to low multiples of the recommended daily allowances (RDAs). It also declared that some botanical products are inherently drugs, not dietary supplements, and that many other dietary supplements, including amino acids, are unapproved food additives.

The Dykstra Report infuriated the public and the dietary supplement industry because the FDA was proposing regulations that either had been prohibited by Congress or struck down in court actions in previous years. The blatant attempt of the FDA, through the Dykstra Report, to ignore the mandate of Congress and the public was a significant motivating factor in efforts to develop and secure passage of the Dietary Supplement Health and Education Act in 1994. During this struggle, more letters protesting the FDA's attempt to restrict access to vitamins were received by members of Congress than on any subject since the war in Vietnam.

When President Clinton signed DSHEA into law in 1994, he said, "In an era of greater consciousness among people about the impact of what they eat on how they live, indeed, on how long they live, it is appropriate that we have finally reformed the way the Government treats consumers and these supplements in a way that encourages good health."[12]

FDA Acts As Though the NAU Already Exists

The FDA has issued 730 warning letters against dietary supplement companies

On October 24, 2005, the FDA issued a press release[13] announcing that "Under a Trilateral Cooperation Charter agreement among Mexico, United States, and Canada signed in 2003, six agencies (two from each country) today announced that they have taken nearly 730 compliance actions against companies that promote bogus weight loss products that mislead the public, endanger the public health, and provide false hope and defraud citizens of billions of dollars."

It continued, "False and misleading claims can have significant health consequences for those who use these products that do not produce the desired results," said Dr. Murray Lumpkin, Deputy Commissioner (International and Special Programs) at the U.S. Food and Drug Administration. "The collaborative efforts of all three countries have contributed to these enforcement actions and we look forward to continuing our trilateral initiatives to make North Americans healthier and able to make better informed health care decisions."

Note the terminology "North Americans." This is the beginning of an effort to cause Canadians, Americans, and Mexicans to stop thinking of themselves as citizens of their respective nations, and to instead think of themselves as "North Americans" much as people in the UK and in all member nations of the European Union are being encouraged to stop identifying themselves as citizens of their respective nations and instead to think of themselves as citizens of the European Union - to which their countries are being forced to harmonize their domestic laws.

In response to a letter from Congressman Ron Paul, which asked hard hitting questions about the supposed "legality" of the FDA's Trilateral Cooperation Charter, the FDA claims that they're "not harmonizing" their regulations with Canada or Mexico - they claim to merely be "exchanging information" with their regulatory counterparts in Canada and Mexico, and they say that this "improves the efficiency" of their enforcement efforts.

They say that any enforcement action taken in Canada, U.S., or Mexico under the auspices of the Trilateral Cooperation Charter is being enforced under the respective laws of each nation, and they deny violating any laws.

FDA says:
"The Canada-Mexico-US Trilateral Cooperation provides the three countries with a formal mechanism to work closely together to better protect, promote and advance human health in North America. Its purpose is to increase communication, collaboration and the exchange of information in the areas of drugs, biologics, medical devices, food safety and nutrition."

"These compliance actions were taken by member agencies of MUCH (Mexico, United States, Canada Health Fraud Working Group), one of several working groups formed by the Trilateral Cooperation Charter. MUCH consists of regulatory officials from health, consumer protection and competition agencies in Mexico [Federal Commission for the Protection from Sanitary Risks (COFEPRIS), Office of the Federal Attorney for Consumer Protection (PROFECO)], the United States (Federal Trade Commission, Food and Drug Administration) and Canada (Health Canada, Competition Bureau).

"The three countries remind consumers that the only way to lose weight is to follow a sensible, well-balanced diet that lowers caloric intake and/or increase physical activity. While certain *prescription products* have been found to be safe and effective in promoting weight loss, the best proven method remains sensible diet and exercise.

"For more information about the MUCH group, the MUCH weight loss initiative and the Trilateral Cooperation Agreement, see the attached Fact Sheet and visit the Trilateral Cooperation website at: www.hc-sc.gc.ca/fn-an/intactivit/trilateral-coop/index_e.html."

Note the emphasis here on *prescription products.* The implication is that no dietary supplement could EVER be safe to use for someone trying to use weight, and its evident here that the Trilateral Cooperation Charter was created as a tool to go after the dietary supplement industry.

FDA's attack on weight-loss products should be viewed in the context of their ban on all dietary supplements containing ephedrine-alkaloid containing dietary supplements, regardless of dose. By attacking ephedra, the FDA sought to protect a multimillion dollar industry in prescription weight loss drugs which are far more dangerous than ephedra (ma huang).

According to The Reader's Digest Family Guide to Natural Medicine, "For thousands of years, practitioners of Chinese medicine have relied on ma-huang tea to treat asthma, flu and even arthritis." Two decades ago Danish investigators found it to be effective for weight loss. Since then millions of consumers have used ephedra/ma huang to lose weight safely.

But, in a move to protect manufacturers of such expensive and dangerous prescription weight-loss drugs as dexfenfluouramine, FDA Deputy Associate Commissioner William Shultz, a long-time opponent of the dietary-supplement industry, said these limits "would essentially prohibit any ephedrine supplement from being used as a weight loss product" (AP 5/2/97)[14]

The legal precedent set by the FDA's banning of even low-dose ephedra products on a basis of arbitrary "risk assessment" could be used to ban any dietary supplement under equally spurious grounds. Given the overly broad definition of "Health Fraud" within the FDA's Trilateral Cooperation Charter, it would appear that the FDA intends to use it as a means of attacking all dietary supplements much in the way they've just attacked ephedra and removed it from the market.

IAHF views regional harmonization via the North American Union and the FDA's Trilateral Cooperation Charter as being the most likely mechanism to be used to usher in even more restrictive measures under development via the UN's Codex Alimentarius Commission. Due to this, we and others are calling for Congressional Oversight on the FDA's Trilateral Cooperation Charter.

We feel that the only chance we have of stopping the North American Union is to awaken the sleeping masses who called Congress in record numbers in 1994 to pass DSHEA and to alert them to contact the Oversight & Investigations Subcommittee of the House Commerce Committee. The only way we're going to get oversight on this issue is if we can flood these offices with a staggering volume of phone calls, faxes, and personal visits.

For this to happen, we must first overcome the spin arrayed against our message by the Natural Products Association (formerly NNFA) which has been taken over by pharmaceutical interests. (See http://www.nocodexgenocide.com/page/page/3112930.htm)

[1] Miguel A. Faria Jr., M.D., *Cuba and the Council on Foreign Relations*, February 15, 2001, www.NewsMax.com, http://www.newsmax.com/archives/articles/2001/2/15/224945.shtml.
[2] http://www.stopthenorthamericanunion.com/TreasonAbounds.html
[3] CBS News, "*Three Amigos Pledge Cooperation*," March 24, 2005, www.cbsnews.com, http://www.cbsnews.com/stories/2005/03/23/politics/main682570.shtml.
[4] White House, *President Meets with President Fox and Prime Minister Martin*, March 28, 2005, www.whitehouse.gov, http://www.whitehouse.gov/news/releases/2005/03/20050323-5.html.
[5] State Department, *North American Leaders Unveil Security and Prosperity Partnership: Bush, Fox, Martin outline trilateral efforts during March 23 meeting*, March 23, 2005, http://usinfo.state.gov/is/Archive/2005/Mar/23-209281.html.
[6] Miguel Pickard, *Trinational Elites Map North American Future in "NAFTA Plus."* August 24, 2005, americas.irc-online, http://americas.irc-online.org/am/386.
[7] FDA's Trilateral Cooperation Charter http://www.fda.gov/oia/charter.html
[8] Canadian Natural Health Products Directorate http://www.hc-sc.gc.ca/dhp-mps/prodnatur/index_e.html
[9] Dietary Supplement Health & Education Act of 1994 http://www.fda.gov/opacom/laws/dshea.html
[10] Ibid 8.
[11] Dykstra Report http://www.lef.org/magazine/mag97/dec-front97.html
[12] Ibid.
[13] FDA Press Release Announces Enforcement Actions Under Trilateral Cooperation Charter http://www.fda.gov/bbs/topics/NEWS/2005/NEW01247.html
[14] http://www.lef.org/magazine/mag97/sept-point97.html
[15] Tenth Circuit Refuses to Hear Ephedra Case- Nutraceutical Appeals to Supreme Court http://www.emord.com/pressrelease/101906.htm
[16][15] http://www.thepetitionsite.com/takeaction/373269232#body

The Maginot Mentality

By Scott C. Tips

After the bloodbath in the fields of France during the First World War in which almost 1.4 million French lives were lost, the Third French Republic was determined that this would never happen again. Vast sums were approved in the 1930s to construct a series of strong forts and powerful buried defensive positions strung in a line on the border between France and its old enemy Germany. This became known as the Maginot Line, named after André Maginot, the French Minister of War at the time; and it is best remembered as a huge failure.

In a literal sense, though, it was not. For although the Germans outflanked the Maginot Line with their massive assault through the undefended Ardennes Forest in May 1940, they never really successfully attacked the Maginot Line itself (with the exception of one of its forts that did fall). The problem was not that the Line was flawed as a concept, the problem was the *mentality* that went with it.

The Maginot Mentality was a French belief that France was safe behind its ultra-modern and advanced protection system. The French, they thought, could relax and breathe easier. And they did, until the whole system, the whole Line, was outflanked; and in a matter of weeks, the French Army, the largest and strongest in Europe up to that point, and the Third French Republic disintegrated and then disappeared into the dustbin of history. The French are now enjoying – somewhat - their *Fifth* French Republic; but they have never forgotten what happened so shockingly fast in 1940.

Nor should we forget. For therein lies a lesson for all of us in the wholefoods industry who fought so hard in the early-to-mid-1990s for the enactment of the Dietary Supplement Health and Education Act of 1994 (DSHEA). DSHEA is nothing but a legislative Maginot Line, and like the Maginot Line, it can be outflanked. Even worse, it can be more easily defeated and eliminated at any time by a mere majority vote of both the House and the Senate.

So Why Do We Feel So Secure?

Many of us in the whole-foods and health-freedom movements from the 1980s remember all too well the arbitrary powers that the Food and Drug Administration (FDA) had in abundance. When it came to dietary supplements, numerous times the FDA would just simply decree that a combination of vitamins and minerals that it did not like constituted a new food "additive" because it was in a new and unique combination. As a food additive, the new combination would be treated under FDA regulations as if it were some toxic chemical and needed to have its safety proved first.

The situation became somewhat worse when in 1990 the Nutrition Labeling and Education Act was passed, an act that was viewed by many as simply tightening FDA control even further over the dietary-supplement industry and, thus, consumers. A backlash amongst consumers resulted and a more pro-health and pro-consumer bill was proposed to rein in the FDA and restrict its arbitrary powers.

Congress was almost literally inundated in an immense outpouring of mail, faxes, and phone calls. In fact, on this issue, Congress received more mail and communications than it had received on any issue since the Vietnam War! DSHEA was the ultimate result. And we have been reaping its health benefits ever since, with the appearance of more innovative products each year (now some 1,000 per year) than was ever contemplated by DSHEA's proponents.

We have had DSHEA now for nearly thirteen years and the wholefoods industry and consumers have grown accustomed to its existence. For the American attention span, thirteen years is a very long time. Both industry and consumers, which have grown, can not envision any way that things will change. They feel secure because the passage of time has been on their side. Bills to limit or eliminate DSHEA have come and gone. Some bills have shown some marginal success at chipping away at the edges of DSHEA; but, in all, the core of DSHEA has never been threatened during its more-than-a-decade-long existence. In a sense, like social security but to a lesser extent, DSHEA has become a "third rail" of politics – untouchable by politicians. Proponents of DSHEA have thus grown fat and sassy about its invulnerability.

The Flank Attack

The opponents of DSHEA, those who would love nothing more than to tell you and me what we should and should not consume, are not stupid. They have long recognized that direct attacks upon DSHEA have not worked and, even worse, can stir up counter-attacks that might even extend the freedoms of DSHEA.

Working carefully, at a distance and invisibly to most Americans, certain of these opponents – primarily the FDA and its pharmaceutical allies – have been setting the stage to outflank DSHEA through a series of interlocking treaty and trade agreements that will require the United States to adopt international food standards that will, **by law,** supplant DSHEA and install instead a regime of vicious and arbitrary controls upon food and food supplements in the United States. DSHEA will be outflanked – indeed, it almost already is – and it will be replaced. Gone will be the freedom for us to manufacture and consume that multitude of healthful substances that we know about. Equally bad, gone will be those many innovative researchers and manufacturers who for a decade now have been discovering and offering us new and more beneficial, natural ways to protect and enhance our health without harmful side effects.

By working through international organizations, treaties, and trade agreements, these opponents can advance their anti-consumer goals more easily because they use unelected bureaucrats and functionaries who are accountable to virtually no one – certainly not to the average citizen. Moreover, by working internationally, the meetings and events at which these actions take place (where treaties, agreements, rules, and "guidelines" are negotiated and drawn up) occur on distant shores and are unusually unreported by the mainstream press. Most Americans and Canadians, let alone the rest of the world, never, ever, hear of these events – unless they are privy to alternative and non-mainstream news.

Regardless, by the time most citizens even become aware of these events, it is or will be far too late for them to do anything about them. That's why this flanking maneuver by DSHEA's opponents is so insidious – when the net is drawn about a largely unsuspecting public, the public will not be able to do anything but submit.

Most Industry Members and
Consumers Are Asleep at the Wheel

Unfortunately, trade associations such as the National Nutritional Foods Association (NNFA), the Council for Responsible Nutrition (CRN), and the International Alliance of Dietary Food Supplement Associations (IADSA) are telling their members that Codex is not a threat to DSHEA and that they need not worry their pretty, little heads about it at all. Most of these associations' members readily accept these statements, trusting in their accuracy. But a great disservice is being done to everyone by this misinformation – some would say disinformation – generated by these trade organizations (members of which are being increasingly purchased by pharmaceutical company interests) because action that could be taken now to head off the implementation of strict Codex guidelines and standards is being deferred until these guidelines and standards become a *fait accompli*.

Most of these associations argue that even if the Codex standards that are finally established are harsh (and indeed they will be far harsher than what is currently permitted in the United States), they will only apply to international trade and can never be imposed on the domestic American market. A few of the associations admit that it would take a trade dispute between the United States and another country to require any domestic legislative change but that since DSHEA gives more liberal requirements than other countries do, these unnamed other countries could never win since their own food-supplements would easily fall within the permitted sales parameters of DSHEA. In short, the argument goes, there would be no trade barriers to the sale of those other countries' goods within the United States.

For the reasons set forth below, the associations' views are wrong. And like a tightly interwoven cloth, many different structures already exist and are being expanded to such an extent that it will be impossible for the domestic laws of any countries to ultimately escape the international food-supplement standards that will descend upon them. The following reasons are not exhaustive and are only intended to provide a general overview of the problems swelling up on the horizon for DSHEA's continued existence.

10 Reasons Why Codex Will Trounce DSHEA

Reason No. 1: The World Trade Organization. Where applicable, the WTO uses Codex texts as a reference point for resolving those international trade disputes where issues pertinent to Codex – such as health and sanitary measures – are at stake, and WTO Members are legally obliged to abide by its rulings. Trade disputes could result in a ruling adverse to the United States requiring a change in domestic American laws. The WTO cannot itself force a change in any member country's domestic laws, but it can levy a monetary or trade sanction that will strongly encourage the member state to repeal or alter the domestic law itself. This event has already occurred in the United States.

Although admittedly speculative, increasingly enhanced international enforcement mechanisms are the trend. Just remember how the WTO's predecessor, GATT, operated for years without even the right to impose sanctions. Now, the WTO can impose trade sanctions. What plans are in store for WTO's successor organization and *its* enhanced powers that we have not even been told about yet? If there is one thing you can be certain of in this World, it is that international organizations such as the WTO are merely way-stations on the greater road to highly-centralized, global institutions that will wield powers previously reserved to national and regional governments. Watch the trend, and the trend here is – and has been for many decades now – towards increasing centralization.

Reason No. 2: The Sanitary and PhytoSanitary Agreement. The SPS Agreement (to which all WTO Members are signatories) permeates international trade. Alarmingly, its Preamble specifically mentions Codex and states that WTO Members (and therefore all SPS signatories) desire *"to further the use of harmonized sanitary and phytosanitary measures between Members, on the basis of international* *standards, guidelines and recommendations developed by the relevant international organizations, including the Codex Alimentarius Commission."*

Then, Article 3 of the SPS Agreement reads: "To harmonize sanitary and phytosanitary measures on as wide a basis as possible, Members **shall** base their food safety measures on international standards, guidelines or recommendations, where they exist." (emphasis added) Remember that Codex is establishing the international standards for food safety, which standards include vitamin-and-mineral food supplements.

The web is woven tighter with Article 5.1 of the SPS Agreement's provision that: "*1. Members shall ensure that their sanitary or phytosanitary measures are based on an assessment, as appropriate to the circumstances, of the risks to human, animal or plant life or health, taking into account risk assessment techniques developed by the relevant international organizations."* For dietary supplements, then, national authorities are required to take into account risk-assessment techniques developed by "the relevant international organizations" (i.e., Codex) in establishing safety limits on dietary supplements. Such safety limits will necessarily include (at least in the regulators' minds) limits on both supplement potencies and supplement availability. Now that the framework of the *Codex Guidelines for Vitamin and Mineral Food Supplements* has been adopted, risk-analysis numbers to slot into the *Guidelines* are already the topic of discussion at meetings of the Codex Committee on Nutrition and Foods for Special Dietary Uses. One of the areas here that delegations such as South Africa and the National Health Federation have been opposing is the Committee's new focus upon "the development of methodological aspects for **over-dosage** of nutrients." The Committee's application of a toxicological model towards healthful natural substances is alarming evidence of the international trend towards supplement suppression.

<u>Reason No. 3:</u> **The Central American Free Trade Agreement.** Modeled after the "success" of NAFTA, CAFTA is an attempt to create an even larger regional block in the Western Hemisphere on the model of the European Union. Section 6 of CAFTA requires its members to form an SPS Committee for the purpose of insuring ongoing harmonization under the terms of the SPS Agreement. It is important to read the *Agreement* itself and not just the Act so as to

uncover the provisions governing dietary supplements. Sections 6 and 7 further lock-in CAFTA signatories' commitment to the WTO, SPS, and Technical Barriers to Trade (TBT) Agreements. This not only entangles the United States and other signatories in the developing maze of Codex regulations, but it sets the stage for yet further tie-ins in future trade agreements or expansions of trade agreements.

CAFTA also provides that within 30 days of its passage, an intergovernmental committee must convene and work to assist the seven signatory governments in carrying out their obligations under the WTO and SPS Agreement. Cleverly, the word "harmonization" is not to be found directly in CAFTA's Section 6; but it is of course found in Section 3 of the SPS Agreement itself, to which later agreement CAFTA refers.

CAFTA is yet another puzzle piece that is intended to fit into place so as to require domestic harmonization to international Codex standards.

Reason No. 4: **The FDA.** FDA's own policy and mindset requires harmonization and the eventual elimination or emasculation of DSHEA. The United States *Federal Register*, October 11, 1995, specifically describes FDA's policy on the development and use of standards for the international harmonization of regulatory requirements and guidelines. In there, FDA states that *"where a relevant international standard exists, or completion is imminent, it will generally be used in preference to a domestic standard . . . .."* This dovetails with FDA's actions time after tiring time at Codex meetings where they have done nothing – or at most almost nothing for cosmetic purposes – to protect consumer access to dietary supplements. Indeed, at these meetings, the FDA functionaries are often the ones leading the grand charge towards harmonization!

Most recently, the FDA and the Federal Trade Commission (FTC) have entered into the so-called Trilateral Cooperation Charter, a form of regulatory "handshakes" with their counterpart agencies in Canada and Mexico to conduct joint enforcement activities across national borders and to further the partnership that the chief executives of those three countries are fostering on many levels, not just on a dietary-supplement level. Neither Canada nor Mexico has DSHEA-type laws and any further harmonization towards those countries' systems of dietary-supplement regulation will be antithetical to DSHEA.

Reason No. 5: **The Free Trade Agreement of the Americas.** An expansion of the CAFTA idea, which in turn was an expansion of the NAFTA idea, the Free Trade Agreement of the Americas (FTAA) is yet another tightening of the net. Not surprisingly, its Articles 19 and 20 mandate U.S. harmonization to the standards of "relevant international organizations." The existence of FTAA and its being fostered on an unsuspecting public by politicians and the mainstream media is just yet further proof that we are not done with the "harmonization" agenda. It's a process that is ongoing, and to which we are only allowed to know what they want us to know – unless we ferret out the information ourselves.

Reason No. 6: **The Codex Procedural Manual.** In 2004, over the NHF's strong objections, the Codex Committee on General Principles (CCGP) decided to recommend to the Commission that the notification-and-acceptance procedures from the Codex Procedural Manual be deleted. Prior to this act, three levels of acceptance for Codex texts had existed (acceptance, rejection, acceptance with changes); and countries were accordingly permitted to notify the Commission as to which level of acceptance they would apply to each individual Codex standard within their territories. With that provision now gone, a fact rubber-stamped later by the Commission in its subsequent meeting, the already-thin veneer of Codex's "voluntary" nature was stripped away. In short, the Codex officials and its member States no longer see a need for "acceptance" procedures when the Guidelines will be deemed automatically accepted by them regardless.

Reason No. 7: **The CCNFSDU Guidelines for Vitamin and Mineral Food Supplements.** The text of the *Codex Guidelines for Vitamin and Mineral Food Supplements* supports the mandatory application of the Guidelines within the jurisdictions of its member States. Specifically, the *Guidelines* states in its Paragraph 1.2 that "These Guidelines *do apply* in those jurisdictions where products defined in 2.1 [i.e., vitamin-and-mineral food supplements] are regulated as foods." (emphasis added). Because the United States is one of those jurisdictions that regulates dietary supplements as a food, the

Guidelines will and do apply.

Codex's importance stretches back to 1985, when the United Nations adopted UN Resolution No. 39/85, which resolution adopted guidelines for consumer-protection policies. Among other things, this Resolution highlights the fact that "Governments should take into account the need of all consumers for food security and should support and, as far as possible, adopt standards from the . . . Codex Alimentarius."

<u>Reason No. 8:</u> **The Actions and Statements of Codex Officials.** During the November 2004 meeting of the Codex Committee on Nutrition and Foods for Special Dietary Uses in Bonn, Germany, I specifically and directly asked (on behalf of the National Health Federation) Dr. Rolf Grossklaus, the CCNFSDU chairman, for either the text of the *Guidelines* or the Committee's Final Report of the meeting to state whether or not it was mandatory for member countries to implement the *Guidelines*. As I recall, Dr. Jeronimas Maskeliunas, one of the Codex officials, answered me by stating that none of the documents that the Committee is developing are "mandatory." He also noted that "member countries decide how to use them." Yet, upon presentation of the Final Report for review and comment by the delegates and observers, there was absolutely no mention made of either the NHF's question or the response. Dr. Rolf Grossklaus refused NHF's request that the matter be included in the Report and gave no good reason for the refusal. For all official intents and purposes, then, there is no record of this statement and raises serious questions as to why it was kept from the record.

<u>Reason No. 9:</u> **Judicial Activism.** American judges are increasingly looking to international law in making their decisions. *"Judges in the United States,"* U.S. Supreme Court Justice Ginsburg noted in her address to the Constitutional Court of South Africa, *"are free to consult all manner of commentary—restatements, treaties, what law professors or even law students write copiously in law reviews. For example, if we can count those writings, why not the analysis of a question similar to the one we confront contained in an opinion of the Supreme Court of Canada, the Constitutional Court of South Africa, the German Constitutional Court, or the European Court of Human Rights? ... The notion that it is improper to look beyond the borders of the United States in*

*grappling with hard questions . . . is in line with the view of the US
Constitution as a document essentially frozen."* This underscores the
fact that the American judicial system will be, and has increasingly
become, friendly and accustomed to the idea that international law
should be applied domestically. This incredible sea change in the
application of U.S. laws by the judicial system does not bode well for
DSHEA in the face of any eventual legal challenge to it or any part
of it.

Reason No. 10: Given all of the above, indicative of a web of interlocking treaties, trade agreements, executive "handshakes," and
other actions taken without our real approval or even oftentimes
knowledge, the foremost reason that DSHEA is threatened is
because all of the above events, actions, and mindsets are creating an
atmosphere no longer conducive to guarding national integrity. The
continued development of international institutions such as Codex
and the WTO (and its eventual successors) as well as the relationships between and among Codex and national authorities regulating
the food and food-supplement markets virtually ensure fertile ground
for thinking antithetical to DSHEA. Rather, the future environment, unless this trend is reversed and reversed soon, will be to "harmonize" our regulatory regime (which includes DSHEA) to those of
the bulk of the World that treats supplements more like drugs. The
pressure will be enormous to do so, and there are enough persons
domestically who will support this agenda to act as 5th Columnists to
drag us down to this lesser-level of freedom. This is the ultimate reality that must be dealt with.

Still Fighting The Last War

Charitably, let me write that, like the French in 1939-1940, the
current trade associations and related hangers-on are still fighting the
last war. These supposedly pro-health-freedom organizations and
people remember the victory of 1994. They remember how they
won that war and now feel secure behind DSHEA. Some even argue
that any severe threat to DSHEA will result in a rapid mobilization
of opposition that will crush any anti-DSHEA proponents and their
actions. Like the French in 1940, however, the Americans do not
see the Germans outflanking them.

About the Authors

Alex Dybring
Alex is a Danish alternative healthcare practitioner and health editor. He has been an active member of MayDay since 1995 and quite active in the quest for health freedom.

Ingrid Franzon
Ingrid is a British-Norwegian, Certified Nutritional Practitioner who lives in Falun, Sweden and works at her Integrated Functional Medicine (IFM) clinic. Ingrid is a well-respected writer of instructional materials and six books on the subjects of nutrition, functional medicine, and ecological health (including her latest book *Yellow Canary Alert*, which is about environmental toxins and how to detoxify and regain good health). She is also an instructor at the Nordic Nutrition and Phytotherapy School (NNFS), a college of nutritional therapy and phytotherapy in Sweden. The editor of *www.YellowCanaries.com* and formerly a Montessori teacher, Ingrid has a particular interest in helping students who experience learning difficulties resulting from exposure to toxins and nutritional imbalances. She first started working in nutritional medicine and natural health care in Zimbabwe, Africa. More recently, she has organized symposia and spoken at professional conferences in the European Union as well as pursued her private practice, consulting with clients of all ages. Ingrid led the NHF delegation at the 28th Session of the Codex Committee on Nutrition and Foods for Special Dietary Uses meeting held in Chiang Mai, Thailand in November 2006, and also represented health-freedom interests on the NHF delegation at the 2007 GMO foods meeting of interested Codex parties.

John C. Hammell
The founder of IAHF, John Hammell has been fighting professionally for health freedom for 18 years, and first got involved with alternative medicine after recovering from a life-threatening illness in 1980 via a suppressed alternative treatment mode (orthomolecular medicine) after mainstream methods almost killed him. His personal belief is that herbs and other dietary supplements are gifts to us all from our Creator. As such, he believes it to be highly immoral for anyone to try to restrict their availability or to do anything that would hamper consumer access. In an article in the September 1996 issue of *Life Extension Magazine*, John was the first to call the Codex Alimentarius International Threat to Health Freedom to public attention. He was also the first to call this issue to the attention of Dr. Matthias Rath. He was on the U.S. Delegation to the Codex Commission's Committee on Nutrition and Foods for Special Dietary Uses in 1996 and 1998 at meetings in Bonn, and Berlin, Germany. For more of an insight on John Hammell read his articles "Why I Fight for Health Freedom" and "Urgent Appeal From An Orthomolecular Psychiatric Survivor: Vitamin Access Threatened Globally." http://www.nocodexgenocide.com

Sepp Hasslberger
Born in Bavaria, in what used to be called West Germany, his education was centered on commerce and the hotel trade, but after some years in Munich and Copenhagen, he moved to Italy together with his wife Susan and they have since been living in Rome for the past 25 years. His work is health related, importing healthy nutritional products into Italy. The diminishing freedoms of natural healing made it imperative that he became active in the international legislative fight for the preservation of natural, nutrition-based methods of health care. His work for health freedom at first involved various industry associations and in more recent years the consumer-oriented association La Leva di Archimede, as well as his blog-site Health Supreme. His views are influenced by L. Ron Hubbard of

"Scientology" fame, by Silvio Gesell's "Natural Economic Order," by Viktor Schauberger, the "Water Wizard" of early 20th-Century Austria, and by "Spaceship Earth" Buckminster Fuller, the gentle giant and prolific discoverer of synergy and tensegrity. He believes that mankind must get ready for its transit into a new space age, as we are not alone in this Universe, but before we can become part of what some call "the galactic community of sentient beings," we must put barbarism behind us and show that we can take care of ourselves and our planet. To start agitating for change, Sepp has identified certain areas that need change, which are described in an article on his Health Supreme website: "Genova, the Azores and our Common Future." He believes the best way to achieve change is communication, and in order to figure out where we should be directing our energies for that coming transition, he has joined a Communication Agents group.

Tamara Thérèsa Mosegaard

An artist, healing massage therapist and psychotherapist using flower remedies, and a healthwriter and inspirator, Tamara Thérèsa has been active in the Danish civil health rights movement, MayDay, since 1997, writing articles and newsletters, being a campaigner, networker, a spokeswoman, and webeditor – and since January 2006 a chairwoman. She has been involved in the field of healing and personal growth for more than 20 years, working with local radio broadcasting for 9 years, hosting roundtable talks about integrated medicine, complementary prevention, psychotherapeutic support, and healing methods. Tamara Thérèsa has created a self-help group for people with "htlv3" (today "hiv") and "aids" called "Alternative Self Help" (ASH) in 1984, has co-started the associations "Aids Alternative" in 1988 and the "Sunbeams" in 1997 – both Danish associations for people affected by the "hiv" and "aids" syndromes. An active international health-freedom networker since 2000, cooperating with the NHF in its Codex work, serving on the NHF Advisory Board, and a Codex-spokeswoman on the GM food issue. Currently, she serves on the board of the Danish "Alternative Cancer Fund" (DAK). For some ten years, she used to work as a psychosocial consultant for people with hiv, aids, cancer, and dementia for a Danish hospital, while offering massage, healing, psychotherapy, and flower remedies to personal clients. Then, she began writing for the international health website "Vitaviva," became a secretary to the Danish Vitality Council, and then a research worker and secretary to the Danish Institute for Orthomolecular Medicine. After witnessing how many sick people have often succumbed to symptom-relieving medicines instead of creating long-term, optimal health by finding the true cause of their suffering, she now networks to increase insight, healing, joy, and personal transformation, as she is convinced that all sickness can be healed psycho-physically by regression and body therapy, detoxification, super nutrition – and simply by bettering one's personal life quality.

Susan J. Negus, Ph.D. is president of Dreamous Corporation USA. A graduate of the University of Southern California, she has a strong background and education in business and holistic health and has dedicated her life to helping people live a healthier life. Dr. Negus is Treasurer of the American Holistic Health Association Board of Directors, a member of the Advisory Board of the National Health Federation, and Treasurer of the Board of Directors of the Foundation for Health Research. She attended the November 2001 and November 2002 sessions of the Codex Committee on Nutrition and Foods for Special Dietary Uses. She has appeared on national and international television promoting health of body and spirit and done radio shows on HGH and other healthy living modalities. For more information go to www.dreamous.com.

Maureen Kennedy Salaman
Long-time president of the National Health Federation, Maureen passed away in August 2006, after having written her Introduction to this then-unpublished work. A prolific healthwriter and dynamic speaker who could attract and vividly motivate literally millions of readers and listeners, Maureen had accomplishments that could literally fill volumes. For

over a quarter of a century, she dedicated herself to one goal: Empowering people with the information necessary to maximize their personal health and well being. Her life-enhancing messages encompass her combination of talents and capabilities that have impacted millions of readers of her books, articles, tapes, television viewers, and live audiences around the World. And that empowerment included fighting strongly for health freedom. It was Maureen, as then-president of the NHF, who strongly supported the NHF's many efforts at Codex.

Paul Anthony Taylor

The Chairman of the National Health Federation is Paul Anthony Taylor, whose background is in the music industry, working as a musician with artists including Sir Paul McCartney and Bill Withers. Starting in 2003, Paul has attended numerous Codex Alimentarius meetings as a member of the NHF delegation and has rapidly accumulated in-depth expertise as to Codex's structure, organization, and operating methods. Most recently, Paul headed up the NHF delegation to the 2006 Codex Alimentarius Commission meeting in Geneva, Switzerland. A meticulous researcher, he has also authored many widely-read articles on the subject of health, health freedom, and Codex. Currently, he is a consultant for the Dr. Rath Foundation and the editor of its magazine.

Scott C. Tips

The current President of the National Health Federation (NHF) is Scott C. Tips, who, since 1989, has also served as its General Counsel. Wearing other organizational hats, Scott also acts as the NHF Treasurer and the Editor of its quarterly journal *Health Freedom News*. A California-licensed attorney and graduate of the University of California at Berkeley School of Law, he was admitted to the California Bar in 1980 and has specialized since 1983 in food-and-drug law and trademark law, but also engages

in business litigation, general business law, and nonprofit organiza
tions, with an international clientele. A writer and journalist, he
writes a regular legal column for *Whole Foods Magazine* called "Legal
Tips," a column he started in 1984. Scott is probably mostly known
for heading up the NHF delegations at various Codex meetings and
being the nearly-lone voice at those meetings for pro-health-freedom
views. His involvement and attendance at those meetings has been
continuous and extensive since June 2000. Many of his articles
appear on the NHF website at *www.thenhf.com*. He may be reached
at sct@thenhf.com.

Suzan Walter

Suzan Walter, MBA, is the co-founder and current
president of the American Holistic Health
Association (AHHA). Suzan has also served as president of the American Holistic Medical Foundation
from 1988-1990. In addition to her volunteer work
for AHHA, she has a private consulting practice spe-
cializing in health and wellness-related organizations and projects on
the Internet – such as Hellerwork International and HealthWorld
Online. With respect to Codex Alimentarius, Suzan has researched
how it and the World Trade Organization function and has applied
this information so as to track the potential impact of the document
Codex Guidelines for Vitamin and Mineral Food Supplements. She
attended the Codex Committee on Nutrition and Foods for Special
Dietary Uses sessions as an observer in 2002, 2003, and 2004, and
continues working to try to validate true facts in the face of conflict-
ing information being presented by opposing groups. Suzan created
an educational website, www.codexinfo.org, to explain these matters
to the U.S. public and to offer a variety of points of view. She may
be reached at codex@ahha.org.

APPENDICES

GUIDELINES FOR VITAMIN AND MINERAL FOOD SUPPLEMENTS
CAC/GL 55 - 2005

PREAMBLE

Most people who have access to a balanced diet can usually obtain all the nutrients they require from their normal diet. Because foods contain many substances that promote health, people should therefore be encouraged to select a balanced diet from food before considering any vitamin and mineral supplement. In cases where the intake from the diet is insufficient or where consumers consider their diet requires supplementation, vitamin and mineral food supplements serve to supplement the daily diet.

1. 1. SCOPE

1.1 These guidelines apply to vitamin and mineral food supplements intended for use in supplementing the daily diet with vitamins and/or minerals.

1.2 Food supplements containing vitamins and/or minerals as well as other ingredients should also be in conformity with the specific rules on vitamins and minerals laid down in these Guidelines.

1.3 These Guidelines apply only in those jurisdictions where products defined in 2.1 are regulated as foods.

1.4 Foods for special dietary uses as defined in the General Standard for the Labelling of and Claims for Prepackaged Foods for Special Dietary Uses (CODEX STAN 146-1985) are not covered by these Guidelines.

2. DEFINITIONS

2.1 Vitamin and mineral food supplements for the purpose of these guidelines derive their nutritional relevance primarily from the minerals and/or vitamins they contain. Vitamin and mineral food supplements are sources in concentrated forms of those nutrients alone or in combinations, marketed in forms such as capsules, tablets, powders, solutions etc., that are designed to be taken in measured small-unit quantities[1] but are not in a conventional food form and whose purpose is to supplement the intake of vitamins and/or minerals from the normal diet.

3. COMPOSITION

3.1 SELECTION OF VITAMINS AND MINERALS

3.1.1 Vitamin and mineral food supplements should contain vitamins/provitamins and minerals whose nutritional value for human beings has been proven by scientific data and whose status as vitamins and minerals is recognised by FAO and WHO.

3.1.2 The sources of vitamins and minerals may be either natural or synthetic and their selection should be based on considerations such as safety and bioavailability. In addition, purity criteria should take into account FAO/WHO standards, or if FAO/WHO standards are not available, international Pharmacopoeias or recognized international standards. In the absence of criteria from these sources, national legislation may be used.

---

[1] This refers to the physical forms of the vitamin and mineral food supplements not to the potency of the supplements.

3.1.3 Vitamin and mineral food supplements may contain all vitamins and minerals that comply with the criteria in 3.1.1, a single vitamin and/or mineral or an appropriate combination of vitamins and/or minerals.

3.2   Contents of vitamins and minerals

3.2.1 The minimum level of each vitamin and/or mineral contained in a vitamin and mineral food supplement per daily portion of consumption as suggested by the manufacturer should be 15% of the recommended daily intake as determined by FAO/WHO.

3.2.2 Maximum amounts of vitamins and minerals in vitamin and mineral food supplements per daily portion of consumption as recommended by the manufacturer shall be set, taking the following criteria into account:

> (a) upper safe levels of vitamins and minerals established by scientific risk assessment based on generally accepted scientific data, taking into consideration, as appropriate, the varying degrees of sensitivity of different consumer groups;

> (b) the daily intake of vitamins and minerals from other dietary sources.

When the maximum levels are set, due account may be taken of the reference intake values of vitamins and minerals for the population. This provision should not lead to setting of maximum levels that are solely based on recommended nutrient intakes (e. g. Population Reference Intake or Recommended Daily Allowance values).

4.   PACKAGING

4.1   The product shall be packed in containers which will safeguard the hygienic and other qualities of the food.

4.2   The containers, including packaging material, shall be made only of substances which are safe and suitable for their intended use. Where the Codex Alimentarius Commission has established a standard for any such substance used as packaging material, that standard shall apply.

5.   LABELLING

5.1   Vitamin and mineral food supplements should be labelled according to the Codex Standard for the Labelling of Prepackaged Foods (Codex-Stan 1-1985, Rev. 1-1991) as well as according to the General Guidelines on Claims (CAC/GL 1-1979).

5.2   The name of the product shall be "food supplement" with an indication of the category(ies) of nutrients or of the individual vitamin(s) and/or mineral(s) contained in the product as the case may be.

5.3   The amount of the vitamins and minerals present in the product should be declared in the labelling in numerical form. The units to be used should be units of weight consistent with the Codex Guidelines on Nutrition Labelling (CAC/GL 2-1985 Rev.1-1993).

5.4   The amounts of the vitamins and minerals declared should be those per portion of the product as recommended for daily consumption and if different, the amount per unit for single use may also be given.

5.5   Information on vitamins and minerals should also be expressed as a percentage of the nutrient reference values mentioned, as the case may be, in the Codex Guidelines on Nutrition Labelling.

5.6   The label should indicate how the product should be used (quantity, frequency, special conditions).

5.7   The label shall contain advice to the consumer not to exceed the maximum one-day amount.

5.8   The label should not state or imply that supplements can be used for the replacement of meals or a varied diet.

5.9   The label shall contain a statement that the product should be stored out of reach of young children.

DIRECTIVE 2002/46/EC OF THE EUROPEAN PARLIAMENT AND OF THE COUNCIL
of 10 June 2002
on the approximation of the laws of the Member States relating to food supplements

(Text with EEA relevance)

THE EUROPEAN PARLIAMENT AND THE COUNCIL OF THE EUROPEAN UNION,

Having regard to the Treaty establishing the European Community, and in particular Article 95 thereof,

Having regard to the proposal from the Commission ([1]),

Having regard to the opinion of the Economic and Social Committee ([2]),

Acting in accordance with the procedure laid down in Article 251 of the Treaty ([3]),

Whereas:

(1) There is an increasing number of products marketed in the Community as foods containing concentrated sources of nutrients and presented for supplementing the intake of those nutrients from the normal diet.

(2) Those products are regulated in Member States by differing national rules that may impede their free movement, create unequal conditions of competition, and thus have a direct impact on the functioning of the internal market. It is therefore necessary to adopt Community rules on those products marketed as foodstuffs.

(3) An adequate and varied diet could, under normal circumstances, provide all necessary nutrients for normal development and maintenance of a healthy life in quantities which meet those established and recommended by generally acceptable scientific data. However, surveys show that this ideal situation is not being achieved for all nutrients and by all groups of the population across the Community.

(4) Consumers, because of their particular lifestyles or for other reasons, may choose to supplement their intake of some nutrients through food supplements.

(5) In order to ensure a high level of protection for consumers and facilitate their choice, the products that will be put on to the market must be safe and bear adequate and appropriate labelling.

(6) There is a wide range of nutrients and other ingredients that might be present in food supplements including, but not limited to, vitamins, minerals, amino acids, essential fatty acids, fibre and various plants and herbal extracts.

(7) As a first stage, this Directive should lay down specific rules for vitamins and minerals used as ingredients of food supplements. Food supplements containing vitamins or minerals as well as other ingredients should also be in conformity with the specific rules on vitamins and minerals laid down in this Directive.

(8) Specific rules concerning nutrients, other than vitamins and minerals, or other substances with a nutritional or physiological effect used as ingredients of food supplements should be laid down at a later stage, provided that adequate and appropriate scientific data about them become available. Until such specific Community rules are adopted and without prejudice to the provisions of the Treaty, national rules concerning nutrients or other substances with nutritional or physiological effect used as ingredients of food supplements, for which no Community specific rules have been adopted, may be applicable.

(9) Only vitamins and minerals normally found in, and consumed as part of, the diet should be allowed to be present in food supplements although this does not mean that their presence therein is necessary. Controversy as to the identity of those nutrients that could potentially arise should be avoided. Therefore, it is appropriate to establish a positive list of those vitamins and minerals.

(10) There is a wide range of vitamin preparations and mineral substances used in the manufacture of food supplements currently marketed in some Member States that have not been evaluated by the Scientific Committee on Food and consequently are not included in the positive lists. These should be submitted to the European Food Safety Authority for urgent evaluation, as soon as appropriate files are presented by the interested parties.

([1]) OJ C 311 E, 31.10.2000, p. 207 and
       C 180 E, 26.6.2001, p. 248.
([2]) OJ C 14, 16.1.2001, p. 42.
([3]) Opinion of the European Parliament of 14 February 2001 (OJ C 276, 1.10.2001, p. 126), Council Common Position of 3 December 2001 (OJ C 90 E, 16.4.2002, p. 1) and Decision of the European Parliament of 13 March 2002. Council Decision of 30 May 2002.

(11) The chemical substances used as sources of vitamins and minerals in the manufacture of food supplements should be safe and also be available to be used by the body. For this reason, a positive list of those substances should also be established. Such substances as have been approved by the Scientific Committee on Food, on the basis of the said criteria, for use in the manufacture of foods intended for infants and young children and other foods for particular nutritional uses can also be used in the manufacture of food supplements.

(12) In order to keep up with scientific and technological developments it is important to revise the lists promptly, when necessary. Such revisions would be implementing measures of a technical nature and their adoption should be entrusted to the Commission in order to simplify and expedite the procedure.

(13) Excessive intake of vitamins and minerals may result in adverse effects and therefore necessitate the setting of maximum safe levels for them in food supplements, as appropriate. Those levels must ensure that the normal use of the products under the instructions of use provided by the manufacturer will be safe for the consumer.

(14) When maximum levels are set, therefore, account should be taken of the upper safe levels of the vitamins and minerals, as established by scientific risk assessment based on generally acceptable scientific data, and of intakes of those nutrients from the normal diet. Due account should also be taken of reference intake amounts when setting maximum levels.

(15) Food supplements are purchased by consumers for supplementing intakes from the diet. In order to ensure that this aim is achieved, if vitamins and minerals are declared on the label of food supplements, they should be present in the product in a significant amount.

(16) The adoption of the specific values for maximum and minimum levels for vitamins and minerals present in food supplements, based on the criteria set out in this Directive and appropriate scientific advice, would be an implementing measure and should be entrusted to the Commission.

(17) General labelling provisions and definitions are contained in Directive 2000/13/EC of the European Parliament and of the Council of 20 March 2000 on the approximation of the laws of the Member States relating to the labelling, presentation and advertising of foodstuffs (¹), and do not need to be repeated. This Directive should therefore be confined to the necessary additional provisions.

(¹) OJ L 109, 6.5.2000, p. 29.

(18) Council Directive 90/496/EEC of 24 September 1990 on nutrition labelling for foodstuffs (²) does not apply to food supplements. Information relating to nutrient content in food supplements is essential for allowing the consumer who purchases them to make an informed choice and use them properly and safely. That information should, in view of the nature of those products, be confined to the nutrients actually present and be compulsory.

(19) Given the particular nature of food supplements, additional means to those usually available to monitoring bodies should be available in order to facilitate efficient monitoring of those products.

(20) The measures necessary for the implementation of this Directive should be adopted in accordance with Council Decision 1999/468/EC of 28 June 1999 laying down the procedures for the exercise of implementing powers conferred on the Commission (³),

HAVE ADOPTED THIS DIRECTIVE:

Article 1

1. This Directive concerns food supplements marketed as foodstuffs and presented as such. These products shall be delivered to the ultimate consumer only in a pre-packaged form.

2. This Directive shall not apply to medicinal products as defined by Directive 2001/83/EC of the European Parliament and of the Council of 6 November 2001 on the Community code relating to medicinal products for human use (⁴).

Article 2

For the purposes of this Directive:

(a) 'food supplements' means foodstuffs the purpose of which is to supplement the normal diet and which are concentrated sources of nutrients or other substances with a nutritional or physiological effect, alone or in combination, marketed in dose form, namely forms such as capsules, pastilles, tablets, pills and other similar forms, sachets of powder, ampoules of liquids, drop dispensing bottles, and other similar forms of liquids and powders designed to be taken in measured small unit quantities;

(b) 'nutrients' means the following substances:

  (i) vitamins,

  (ii) minerals.

(²) OJ L 276, 6.10.1990, p. 40.
(³) OJ L 184, 17.7.1999, p. 23.
(⁴) OJ L 311, 28.11.2001, p. 67.

Article 3

Member States shall ensure that food supplements may be marketed within the Community only if they comply with the rules laid down in this Directive.

Article 4

1. Only vitamins and minerals listed in Annex I, in the forms listed in Annex II, may be used for the manufacture of food supplements, subject to paragraph 6.

2. The purity criteria for substances listed in Annex II shall be adopted in accordance with the procedure referred to in Article 13(2), except where they apply pursuant to paragraph 3.

3. Purity criteria for substances listed in Annex II, specified by Community legislation for their use in the manufacture of foodstuffs for purposes other than those covered by this Directive, shall apply.

4. For those substances listed in Annex II for which purity criteria are not specified by Community legislation, and until such specifications are adopted, generally acceptable purity criteria recommended by international bodies shall be applicable and national rules setting stricter purity criteria may be maintained.

5. Modifications to the lists referred to in paragraph 1 shall be adopted in accordance with the procedure referred to in Article 13(2).

6. By way of derogation from paragraph 1 and until 31 December 2009, Member States may allow in their territory the use of vitamins and minerals not listed in Annex I, or in forms not listed in Annex II, provided that:

(a) the substance in question is used in one or more food supplements marketed in the Community on the date of entry into force of this Directive,

(b) the European Food Safety Authority has not given an unfavourable opinion in respect of the use of that substance, or its use in that form, in the manufacture of food supplements, on the basis of a dossier supporting use of the substance in question to be submitted to the Commission by the Member State not later than 12 July 2005.

7. Notwithstanding paragraph 6, Member States may, in compliance with the rules of the Treaty, continue to apply existing national restrictions or bans on trade in food supplements containing vitamins and minerals not included in the list in Annex I or in the forms not listed in Annex II.

8. Not later than 12 July 2007, the Commission shall submit to the European Parliament and the Council a report on the advisability of establishing specific rules, including, where appropriate, positive lists, on categories of nutrients or of substances with a nutritional or physiological effect other than those referred to in paragraph 1, accompanied by any proposals for amendment to this Directive which the Commission deems necessary.

Article 5

1. Maximum amounts of vitamins and minerals present in food supplements per daily portion of consumption as recommended by the manufacturer shall be set, taking the following into account:

(a) upper safe levels of vitamins and minerals established by scientific risk assessment based on generally accepted scientific data, taking into account, as appropriate, the varying degrees of sensitivity of different consumer groups;

(b) intake of vitamins and minerals from other dietary sources.

2. When the maximum levels referred to in paragraph 1 are set, due account should also be taken of reference intakes of vitamins and minerals for the population.

3. To ensure that significant amounts of vitamins and minerals are present in food supplements, minimum amounts per daily portion of consumption as recommended by the manufacturer shall be set, as appropriate.

4. The maximum and minimum amounts of vitamins and minerals referred to in paragraphs 1, 2 and 3 shall be adopted in accordance with the procedure referred to in Article 13(2).

Article 6

1. For the purposes of Article 5(1) of Directive 2000/13/EC, the name under which products covered by this Directive are sold shall be 'food supplement'.

2. The labelling, presentation and advertising must not attribute to food supplements the property of preventing, treating or curing a human disease, or refer to such properties.

3. Without prejudice to Directive 2000/13/EC, the labelling shall bear the following particulars:

(a) the names of the categories of nutrients or substances that characterise the product or an indication of the nature of those nutrients or substances;

(b) the portion of the product recommended for daily consumption;

(c) a warning not to exceed the stated recommended daily dose;

(d) a statement to the effect that food supplements should not be used as a substitute for a varied diet;

(e) a statement to the effect that the products should be stored out of the reach of young children.

Article 7

The labelling, presentation and advertising of food supplements shall not include any mention stating or implying that a balanced and varied diet cannot provide appropriate quantities of nutrients in general.

Rules for implementing this Article may be specified in accordance with the procedure referred to in Article 13(2).

Article 8

1. The amount of the nutrients or substances with a nutritional or physiological effect present in the product shall be declared on the labelling in numerical form. The units to be used for vitamins and minerals shall be those specified in Annex I.

Rules for implementing this paragraph may be specified in accordance with the procedure referred to in Article 13(2).

2. The amounts of the nutrients or other substances declared shall be those per portion of the product as recommended for daily consumption on the labelling.

3. Information on vitamins and minerals shall also be expressed as a percentage of the reference values mentioned, as the case may be, in the Annex to Directive 90/496/EEC.

Article 9

1. The declared values mentioned in Article 8(1) and (2) shall be average values based on the manufacturer's analysis of the product.

Further rules for implementing this paragraph with regard in particular to the differences between the declared values and those established in the course of official checks shall be decided upon in accordance with the procedure referred to in Article 13(2).

2. The percentage of the reference values for vitamins and minerals mentioned in Article 8(3) may also be given in graphical form.

Rules for implementing this paragraph may be adopted in accordance with the procedure referred to in Article 13(2).

Article 10

To facilitate efficient monitoring of food supplements, Member States may require the manufacturer or the person placing the product on the market in their territory to notify the competent authority of that placing on the market by forwarding it a model of the label used for the product.

Article 11

1. Without prejudice to Article 4(7), Member States shall not, for reasons related to their composition, manufacturing specifications, presentation or labelling, prohibit or restrict trade in products referred to in Article 1 which comply with this Directive and, where appropriate, with Community acts adopted in implementation of this Directive.

2. Without prejudice to the Treaty, in particular Articles 28 and 30 thereof, paragraph 1 shall not affect national provisions which are applicable in the absence of Community acts adopted under this Directive.

Article 12

1. Where a Member State, as a result of new information or of a reassessment of existing information made since this Directive or one of the implementing Community acts was adopted, has detailed grounds for establishing that a product referred to in Article 1 endangers human health though it complies with the said Directive or said acts, that Member State may temporarily suspend or restrict application of the provisions in question within its territory. It shall immediately inform the other Member States and the Commission thereof and give reasons for its decision.

2. The Commission shall examine as soon as possible the grounds adduced by the Member State concerned and shall consult the Member States within the Standing Committee on the Food Chain and Animal Health, and shall then deliver its opinion without delay and take appropriate measures.

3. If the Commission considers that amendments to this Directive or to the implementing Community acts are necessary in order to remedy the difficulties mentioned in paragraph 1 and to ensure the protection of human health, it shall initiate the procedure referred to in Article 13(2) with a view to adopting those amendments. The Member State that has adopted safeguard measures may in that event retain them until the amendments have been adopted.

Article 13

1. The Commission shall be assisted by the Standing Committee on the Food Chain and Animal Health instituted by Regulation (EC) No 178/2002 [1] (hereinafter referred to as 'the Committee').

2. Where reference is made to this paragraph, Articles 5 and 7 of Decision 1999/468/EC shall apply, having regard to the provisions of Article 8 thereof.

The period laid down in Article 5(6) of Decision 1999/468/EC shall be set at three months.

3. The Committee shall adopt its rules of procedure.

_____
[1] OJ L 31, 1.2.2002, p. 1.

Article 14

Provisions that may have an effect upon public health shall be adopted after consultation with the European Food Safety Authority.

Article 15

Member States shall bring into force the laws, regulations and administrative provisions necessary to comply with this Directive by 31 July 2003. They shall forthwith inform the Commission thereof.

Those laws, regulations and administrative provisions shall be applied in such a way as to:

(a) permit trade in products complying with this Directive, from 1 August 2003 at the latest;

(b) prohibit trade in products which do not comply with the Directive, from 1 August 2005 at the latest.

When Member States adopt these measures, they shall contain a reference to this Directive or be accompanied by such a reference on the occasion of their official publication. The methods of making such reference shall be adopted by the Member States.

Article 16

This Directive shall enter into force on the day of its publication in the *Official Journal of the European Communities*.

Article 17

This Directive is addressed to the Member States.

Done at Luxembourg, 10 June 2002.

For the European Parliament	*For the Council*
The President	*The President*
P. COX	J. PIQUÉ I CAMPS

———

ANNEX I

Vitamins and minerals which may be used in the manufacture of food supplements

1. Vitamins

   Vitamin A (μg RE)

   Vitamin D (μg)

   Vitamin E (mg α-TE)

   Vitamin K (μg)

   Vitamin B1 (mg)

   Vitamin B2 (mg)

   Niacin (mg NE)

   Pantothenic acid (mg)

   Vitamin B6 (mg)

   Folic acid (μg)

   Vitamin B12 (μg)

   Biotin (μg)

   Vitamin C (mg)

2. Minerals

   Calcium (mg)

   Magnesium (mg)

   Iron (mg)

   Copper (μg)

   Iodine (μg)

   Zinc (mg)

   Manganese (mg)

   Sodium (mg)

   Potassium (mg)

   Selenium (μg)

   Chromium (μg)

   Molybdenum (μg)

   Fluoride (mg)

   Chloride (mg)

   Phosphorus (mg)

———

ANNEX II

Vitamin and mineral substances which may be used in the manufacture of food supplements

A. Vitamins

1. VITAMIN A

   (a) retinol
   (b) retinyl acetate
   (c) retinyl palmitate
   (d) beta-carotene

2. VITAMIN D

   (a) cholecalciferol
   (b) ergocalciferol

3. VITAMIN E

   (a) D-alpha-tocopherol
   (b) DL-alpha-tocopherol
   (c) D-alpha-tocopheryl acetate
   (d) DL-alpha-tocopheryl acetate
   (e) D-alpha-tocopheryl acid succinate

4. VITAMIN K

   (a) phylloquinone (phytomenadione)

5. VITAMIN B1

   (a) thiamin hydrochloride
   (b) thiamin mononitrate

6. VITAMIN B2

   (a) riboflavin
   (b) riboflavin 5'-phosphate, sodium

7. NIACIN

   (a) nicotinic acid
   (b) nicotinamide

8. PANTOTHENIC ACID

   (a) D-pantothenate, calcium
   (b) D-pantothenate, sodium
   (c) dexpanthenol

9. VITAMIN B6

   (a) pyridoxine hydrochloride
   (b) pyridoxine 5'-phosphate

10. FOLIC ACID

    (a) pteroylmonoglutamic acid

11. VITAMIN B12

    (a) cyanocobalamin
    (b) hydroxocobalamin

12. BIOTIN

    (a) D-biotin

13. VITAMIN C

    (a) L-ascorbic acid
    (b) sodium-L-ascorbate
    (c) calcium-L-ascorbate
    (d) potassium-L-ascorbate
    (e) L-ascorbyl 6-palmitate

B. Minerals

calcium carbonate
calcium chloride
calcium salts of citric acid
calcium gluconate
calcium glycerophosphate
calcium lactate
calcium salts of orthophosphoric acid
calcium hydroxide
calcium oxide
magnesium acetate
magnesium carbonate
magnesium chloride
magnesium salts of citric acid
magnesium gluconate
magnesium glycerophosphate
magnesium salts of orthophosphoric acid
magnesium lactate
magnesium hydroxide
magnesium oxide
magnesium sulphate
ferrous carbonate
ferrous citrate
ferric ammonium citrate
ferrous gluconate
ferrous fumarate
ferric sodium diphosphate
ferrous lactate
ferrous sulphate
ferric diphosphate (ferric pyrophosphate)
ferric saccharate
elemental iron (carbonyl+electrolytic+hydrogen reduced)
cupric carbonate
cupric citrate
cupric gluconate
cupric sulphate
copper lysine complex

sodium iodide

sodium iodate

potassium iodide

potassium iodate

zinc acetate

zinc chloride

zinc citrate

zinc gluconate

zinc lactate

zinc oxide

zinc carbonate

zinc sulphate

manganese carbonate

manganese chloride

manganese citrate

manganese gluconate

manganese glycerophosphate

manganese sulphate

sodium bicarbonate

sodium carbonate

sodium chloride

sodium citrate

sodium gluconate

sodium lactate

sodium hydroxide

sodium salts of orthophosphoric acid

potassium bicarbonate

potassium carbonate

potassium chloride

potassium citrate

potassium gluconate

potassium glycerophosphate

potassium lactate

potassium hydroxide

potassium salts of orthophosphoric acid

sodium selenate

sodium hydrogen selenite

sodium selenite

chromium (III) chloride

chromium (III) sulphate

ammonium molybdate (molybdenum (VI))

sodium molybdate (molybdenum (VI))

potassium fluoride

sodium fluoride

Nutrient risk assessment project

The Food and Agriculture Organization of the United Nations (FAO) and the World Health Organization (WHO) plan to convene a technical expert workshop on nutrient risk assessment in May 2005. The outcome of the workshop will be to provide scientific advice to FAO and WHO concerning an internationally applicable approach that may be used as part of future activities to identify safe upper levels of intake for nutrients and related substances. The goal of the workshop is to consider existing approaches as appropriate and develop a model or framework that can be applied by FAO/WHO as well as member countries. The outcome will be a set of scientific guidelines for the purpose of risk assessment only. This risk assessment approach may be considered by national and regional risk managers to the extent it is appropriate to their needs and interests in establishing their own public health policies and regulations.

Plans for the FAO/WHO workshop include soliciting public input for this activity at two points in time. The first request for input occurred between 1 November 2004 and 7 January 2005. On 1 November, FAO/WHO posted a Background Paper on their websites which outlined key issues and the scientific challenges related to nutrient risk assessment. The Background Paper also asked a series of questions. All interested persons were invited to submit comments and responses to the questions through 10 December. The comments received were posted on the website so that all could see the input provided. A Call for Information was also conducted from 1 November to 7 January. Both the comments in response to the Background Paper and the materials received as a result of the Call for Information will be made available to the scientific experts who will take part in the workshop.

The second opportunity for public input will occur at the time the report of the workshop is completed. The report will be posted on the FAO/WHO websites for public comment. Comments received will be taken into consideration before the report is considered for distribution by FAO/WHO.

In order to assist FAO/WHO in identifying scientific experts qualified to take part in the workshop, a Call for Experts was issued and posted on the websites. Applications to be considered to serve as an expert could be submitted electronically or by mail from 24 November until 7 January 2005.

The qualifications for experts were outlined in the Call for Experts. As described in the Call for Experts, qualifications included among other factors training as well as professional experience at the national and/or international level in the areas of nutrition, toxicology, dietary exposure, statistics, food technology, biochemistry, pharmacology and other closely related disciplines. Overall, the selection process will take into account appropriate interdisciplinary balance of expertise as well as equitable geographical representation and gender balance. Should FAO/WHO find that certain expertise is lacking among the pool of candidates, FAO/WHO may seek additional experts to add to the pool of candidates as needed. The selection of workshop participants is conducted collectively by FAO/WHO and is not the responsibility of individual staff members. Persons who made applications in response to the Call for Experts and who are not selected will be notified of their non-selection by e-mail no later than 18 February.

Consistent with the WHO procedures for the meetings of experts, the workshop is of a private character and will not be open to the public. The names of persons selected to serve as workshop experts will not be announced until the workshop report is finalized and distributed.

This web site contains all the information now available about the workshop on nutrient risk assessment. Please note that World Health Organization: Basic Documents (44th ed, October 2002) is available on the WHO web site (http://www.who.int/governance/).

You may also view the responses to the questions posed in the Background Paper:

FAO/WHO have also conducted a Call for Experts to serve as participants in the May 2005 nutrient risk assessment workshop. Information on the Call for Experts was posted on the website and made available to all interested parties. Applications were received electronically as well as by mail through 7 January 2005. The Call for Experts document may be viewed below:

Contact information for the Nutrient Risk Assessment project:

IPCS/Nutrient Risk Assessment
Room L-228
World Health Organization
20, Avenue Appia
CH-1211 Geneva 27
Switzerland

Guidelines for Vitamin and Mineral Food Supplements
Finalized by the Codex Alimentarius Commission July 4, 2005

PREAMBLE
Most people who have access to a balanced diet can usually obtain all the nutrients they require from their normal diet. Because foods contain many substances that promote health, people should therefore by encouraged to select a balanced diet from food before considering any vitamin and mineral supplement. In cases where the intake from the diet is insufficient or where consumers consider their diet requires supplementation, vitamin and mineral food supplements serve to supplement the daily diet.

1. SCOPE
1.1 These guidelines apply to vitamin and mineral food supplements intended for use in supplementing the daily diet with vitamins and/or minerals.
1.2 Food supplements containing vitamins and/or minerals as well as other ingredients should also be in conformity with the specific rules on vitamins and minerals laid down in these Guidelines.
1.3. These Guidelines only apply in those jurisdictions where products defined in 2.1 are regulated as foods.
1.4. Foods for special dietary uses as defined in the General Standard for the Labeling of and Claims for Prepackaged Foods for Special Dietary Uses (CODEX STAN 146-1985) are not covered by these Guidelines.

2. DEFINITIONS
2.1 Vitamin and mineral food supplements for the purpose of these guidelines derive their nutritional relevance primarily from the minerals and/or vitamins they contain. Vitamin and mineral food supplements are sources of concentrated forms of those nutrients alone or in combinations, marketed in forms such as capsules, tablets, powders, solutions, etc.,that are designed to be taken in measured small-unit quantities 1 but are not in a conventional food form and whose purpose is to supplement the intake of vitamins and/or minerals from the normal diet.

3. COMPOSITION
3.1 Selection of vitamins and minerals
3.1.1. Vitamin and mineral food supplements should contain vitamins/provitamins and minerals whose nutritional value for human beings has been proven by scientific data and whose status as vitamins and minerals is recognized by FAO and WHO.
3.1.2. The sources of vitamins and minerals may be either natural or synthetic

and their selection should be based on considerations such as safety and bioavailability. In addition, purity criteria should take into account FAO/WHO standards, or if FAO/WHO standards are not available, international Pharmacopoeias or recognized international standards. In the absence of criteria from these sources, national legislation may be used.

3.1.3 Vitamin and mineral food supplements may contain all vitamins and minerals that comply with the criteria in 3.1.1. a single and/or mineral or an appropriate combination of vitamins and/or minerals.

3.2 Contents of vitamins and minerals

3.2.1 The minimum level of each vitamin and/or mineral contained in a vitamin and mineral food supplement per daily portion of consumption as suggested by the manufacturer should be 15% of the recommended daily intake as determined by FAO/WHO.

3.2.2 Maximum amounts of vitamins and minerals in vitamin and mineral food supplements per daily portion of consumption as recommended by the manufacturer shall be set, taking the following criteria into account:

(a) upper safe levels of vitamins and mineral established by scientific risk assessment based on generally accepted scientific data, taking into consideration, as appropriate, the varying degrees of sensitivity of different consumer groups;

(b) the daily intake of vitamins and minerals from other dietary sources. When the maximum levels are set, due account may be taken of the reference intake values of vitamins and minerals for the population. This provision should not lead to setting of maximum levels that are solely based on recommended nutritient intakes (e.g. Population Reference Intake or Recommended Daily Allowance values).

4. PACKAGING

4.1 The product shall be packed in containers which will safeguard the hygienic and other qualities of the food.

4.2. The containers, including packaging material, shall be made only of substances which are safe and suitable for their intended use. Where the Codex Alimentarius Commission has established a standard for any substance used as packaging material, that standard shall apply.

5. Labeling

5.1 Vitamin and mineral food supplements should be Labeled according to the Codex Standard for the Labeling of Prepackaged Foods (Codex-Stan 1-1985 Rev. 1-1991) as well as according to the General Guidelines on Claims (CAC/GL 1-1979).

5.2 The name of the product shall be "food supplement" with an indication of the category(ies) of nutrients or of the individual vitamin(s) and/or mineral(s) contained in the product as the case may be.

5.3 The amount of the vitamins and minerals present in the product should be declared in the Labeling in numerical form. The units to be used should be units of weight consistent with the Codex Guidelines on Nutrition Labeling.

5.4 The amounts of the vitamins and minerals declared should be those per portion of the product as recommended for daily consumption and if different, the amount per unit for single use may also be given.

5.5 Information on vitamins and minerals should also be expressed as a percentage of the nutrient reference values mentioned, as the case may be, in the Codex Guidelines on Nutrition Labeling.

5.6 The label should indicate how the product should be used (quantity, frequency, special conditions).

5.7 The label shall contain advice to the consumer not to exceed the maximum one-day amount.

5.8 The label should not state or imply that supplements can be used for the replacement of meals or a varied diet.

5.9 The label shall contain a statement that the product should be stored out of the reach of young children.

[1] *This refers to the physical forms of the vitamin and mineral food supplements not to the potency of the supplements.*

NHF NATIONAL HEALTH FEDERATION

JOINT FAO/WHO FOOD STANDARDS PROGRAMME
Codex Committee on Nutrition and Foods for Special Dietary Uses
Comments of the National Health Federation on the Draft Guidelines for Vitamin and Mineral Food Supplements at Step 8 of the Procedure
(ALINORM 05/28/26 para. 35 and Appendix II):

The National Health Federation considers that the drafting of the Guidelines for Vitamin and Mineral Food Supplements has not been carried out in full accordance with the rules set out in the Codex Procedural Manual (14th edition).

Paragraph (b) (page 57) of the section dealing with DRAWING UP OF CODEX STANDARDS (under GUIDE-LINES ON THE CONDUCT OF MEETINGS OF CODEX COMMITTEES AND AD HOC INTERGOVERNMENTAL TASK FORCES) states that:

....all standards and related texts should have a preface containing.....a brief description of the scope and purpose(s) of the standard or related text,

This requirement was agreed at the 19th Session of the Codex Committee on General Principles, held in Paris between 17-21 November 2003, and adopted at the 27th Session of the Codex Alimentarius Commission (CAC), held in Geneva between 28th June and 2nd July 2004. The Codex Committee on Nutrition and Foods for Special Dietary Uses (CCNFSDU) subsequently met in Bonn from 1-5 November 2004 (26th Session) but did not take proper account of this requirement when considering the guidelines, as evidenced by both the CCNFSDU's report of its 26th session and the draft text of the guidelines themselves:

1. The CCNFSDU's report of its 26th Session gives no indication that the requirement for the preface to contain a description of the purpose of the text was even considered, despite the fact that the matter was raised at this session by the delegations of South Africa, Tanzania and the National Health Federation.
2. Neither the Preamble nor the Scope of the guidelines contain any statement to indicate the purpose(s) of the text. Given therefore that Codex texts have been used as the benchmark in international trade disputes, and moreover that it is expected that they will be used increasingly in this regard, we consider that it is of crucial legal importance that the question "What is the purpose of the guidelines?" should have a clear, easily understandable answer, and moreover that this should be provided in the text.

Bearing the above in mind, the National Health Federation believes that the 28th Session of the Codex Alimentarius Commission has no option but to refer the Guidelines for Vitamin and Mineral Food Supplements back to the CCNFSDU, in accordance with the GUIDE TO THE CONSIDERATION OF STANDARDS AT STEP 8 OF THE PROCEDURE FOR THE ELABORATION OF CODEX STANDARDS INCLUDING CONSIDERATION OF ANY STATEMENTS RELATING TO ECONOMIC IMPACT, as described on pages 26-27 of the Codex Procedural Manual (14th edition). As such, until such time as the CCNFSDU's written comments regarding this matter have been received and considered by the CAC the guidelines should not, and indeed, cannot, be advanced beyond Step 8 of the Procedure.

P.O. Box 688, Monrovia, CA 91017 ~ 1 (626) 357-2181 ~ Fax 1 (626) 303-0642
Website: www.thenhf.com   E-mail: contact-us@thenhf.com

BY E-MAIL & FAX TO (202) 720-3157
Dr. Elizabeth Yetley #364.00
U.S. Codex Office
Room 4861, South Building
Washington, D.C. 20250-3700

August 22, 2002

Re: Comments on CCNFSDU CODEX ALIMENTARIUS

Dear Dr. Yetley:

On behalf of the National Health Federation, the nation's oldest nonprofit organization dedicated to ensuring consumers' rights to freedom of choice in food, dietary-supplement and medical matters, we respectfully submit the following comments on the draft guidelines of the Codex Committee on Nutrition and Foods for Special Dietary Uses, due August 23, 2002:/

1. "Positive Lists" for Vitamins & Minerals: While superficially attractive, "positive lists" of "approved" vitamins and minerals, are counterproductive, obsolete before they can even be implemented, and illegal under United States law. Therefore, you have no choice but to strenuously oppose any and all implementation of "positive lists" within the Codex Committee system.

a. Counterproductive. The so-called "positive lists" are counterproductive because they will mislead consumers and governmental bodies into thinking that only those vitamins and minerals appearing on the list are safe and acceptable./ Eventually, if not more immediately, such a list will become the basis of law that only those vitamins and minerals appearing on this list will be allowed to be lawfully sold.

Many vitamins and minerals, or other associated nutrients and co-factors, especially those yet to be fully investigated or even discovered, will not appear on this list because the committee process (particularly the international committee process) will be slow, arduous, and subject to arbitrary dispute by those countries with, frankly, political agendas and/or insufficient sophistication in food matters to support their inclusion. Vitamins and minerals that might otherwise help people nutritionally will be omitted from the list, either forever or for sufficiently long periods of time so as to negatively impact consumers' health.

b. Obsolete Before Publication. Because of the slow process mentioned above in implementing and then publicizing such a list, the current accelerating pace of advances in knowledge of clinical nutrition will make such a list obsolete before it is even fixed and published. Therefore, such a list will be not only counterproductive but backward. It will be the same spirit as mandating gas-lighting standards during the time that electrical lighting was being introduced. Knowledge is not static and what we know today about clinical nutrition is far beyond the knowledge we possessed even in 1985, slightly more than fifteen years ago. And in 15 years' time, today's knowledge on the subject will appear equally quaint.

For this reason, as both a practical matter and a philosophical approach, the free market, not agency edict, is the best mechanism here for maximizing the health of the public.

c. Illegal. The Dietary Supplement Health and Education Act of 1994 ("DSHEA") as well as the anti-harmonization provisions of the FDA Modernization Act of 1997 prohibit positive lists of approved vitamins and minerals. Vitamins and minerals are not "approved" as are drugs; rather, they exist and, except for newly discovered vitamins, they can be freely sold within the United States as dietary supplements provided that they are appropriately labeled and make no disease claims. The publication and use of a positive list of vitamins and minerals would be inconsistent with American law in this regard by its creation of a two-tier system of "approved" vitamins and minerals and "non-approved" vitamins and minerals.

Furthermore, the anti-harmonization provisions of the FDA Modernization Act of 1997 prohibit the Food and Drug Administration from engaging in any action that would subvert DSHEA and/or other existing American law. Agreeing and committing the United States government to such a list would accordingly violate U.S. law.

2. "Negative Lists" for Vitamins & Minerals: Not even superficially attractive, the so-called "negative lists" for prohibited vitamins and minerals have all of the problems mentioned for positive lists. They are counterproductive, obsolete before they can even be implemented, and illegal under United States law. Moreover, negative lists would especially invite abuse, since they would proscribe certain vitamins and minerals, perhaps at certain levels, based upon data that is in dispute. Indeed, even the Food and Drug Administration has yet to define for the Pearson v. Shalala Court the term "substantial scientific agreement."

3. Upper & Lower Potency Limits for Vitamins & Minerals: Subsumed within the positive and negative lists are presumed upper and lower limits for vitamins and minerals. Such limits would suffer from all of the above-mentioned problems and illegalities. It would be exactly the same as bureaucratically prescribing the techniques for manufacturing early airplanes from the 1910s; knowledge advances but the rules governing such prior knowledge, being less elastic, retard the progress of knowledge and, hence, society in general.

Most importantly, United States law flatly prohibits the Secretary from imposing maximum limits on the potency of safe vitamins and minerals. (See the "Proxmire" Amendment of 1976, Pub. L. No. 94-278, §501, 90 Stat. 410.) Read in juxtaposition with the FDA Modernization Act of 1997, this Amendment completely prevents you from agreeing to any maximum limits on vitamin-and-mineral potency, no matter how well meaning or based your intentions might be. You have no choice but to reject upper limits.

Moreover, the practical problem with upper limits is self-evident. First of all, if they are based on common European misconceptions, then they will be far to low to be efficacious in any genuine respect. We rather suspect that that is the true intent. Assuming the best, however, that is, that the motives are sincere, then the concept of upper limits on vitamins and minerals is still greatly misguided because they will be based upon RDIs that were created to avoid deficiencies in those particular vitamins and minerals in general populations, not with the goal of maximizing health in individuals. Those are two very different goals.

Lower limits for vitamins "sound" as if they might be a valid concept, but when you consider the effect, you will also realize that, however well-intentioned, the effect will be equally counterproductive. Consider multivitamin capsules or tablets that, of course, only have a finite amount of capacity available for filling. If a lower limit has been set, but inadequate space remains in which one may fill that space with a particular vitamin or mineral, then the manufacturer must omit that ingredient and substitute a useless filler or excipient instead. The result: the consumer will have lost out on receiving at least some of an important nutrient. Under the philosophy that something is better than nothing, the argument is made here that the consumer will have suffered a loss. It would be indefensible for you to say that you are "protecting" the consumers' health by causing manufacturers' to omit healthful ingredients from their products. Rather, if a genuine concern exists about consumers being misled by their intake amount of a particular vitamin or mineral, then the level can be clearly and adequately disclosed on the product label. That is a situation that already exists and is already addressed with current label laws and regulations.

4. National Authorities Determination of Whether Vitamins & Minerals May be Treated as "Foods" of "Drugs" (Agenda Item 5): The proposed draft guidelines make it clear that most of the Europeans would like vitamin and mineral supplements to be tightly regulated and not to be sold in a free and open market. Therefore, right out of the chute, the draft guidelines are heavily biased to the restrictive European viewpoint: if a country's laws treat vitamin and mineral supplements as drugs, then the Codex guidelines would not apply to those supplements since the Codex guidelines are intended only for food. Therefore, the precious European national laws making drugs out of natural vitamins and minerals would not be touched. The only touchable laws would be those food and dietary supplement laws (such as in the U.S.) that treat vitamins and minerals with actual concern for consumer freedom of choice. The playing field has thus been ipso facto unfairly defined.

5. Substances Must Prove Their Nutritive Value for Humans Before They Can Be Acceptable (Agenda Item 5): The National Health Federation absolutely opposes any provision that would revise the Composition section of the Proposed Draft Guidelines for Vitamin and Mineral Supplements to indicate that substances would only be acceptable if scientific data had proven their nutritive value for human beings and if criteria such as safety and bioavailability were considered in their selection. Such a provision would be absolutely insane! The National Health Federation cannot even believe that anyone would be so ignorant as to propose such a provision.

If someone must first prove the "value" of a substance to humans before it can even be used, then the currently feeble knowledge of humans and incomplete understanding of dietary substances will prevent many useful and important nutritional substances from being available to nourish us until human knowledge catches up with reality. And that may never occur. Moreover, once again we must decide upon what constitutes "value" and how that term is defined. This whole area is a veritable minefield of disasters. You not only should, but you must, fight against any such limiting provision. To do otherwise is to betray your duty to Americans to protect their health.

6. General Comments About Nutrient-Content Claims (Agenda Item 10): The National Health Federation's position is that all dietary supplements, including vitamins and minerals, should be permitted to have labels and labeling that advise consumers of truthful and

ion misleading information about the product.

We know that the official U.S. position has been to push for limits and lists based upon "science-based risk assessment" methods. The question, though, is upon whose "science" will this science-based risk assessment be based? One of the risks in adopting such science-based risk assessment standards is that they will not be fair and objective, but will instead be used to create artificial barriers that will only restrict freedom of choice. And compliance with those standards could be equally difficult if lengthy, expensive, drug-like tests, trials, and clinical studies must first be conducted before the standards are established and implemented. Either way, United States law will be broken if dietary supplements are required to comply with standards different than those already set forth in DSHEA.

While there is merit to the claim that the Europeans would be better off with vitamin-and-mineral potencies based upon a science-based risk assessment standard rather than their current, completely arbitrary standard, the Food and Drug Administration's first priority is not to convert foreign agencies to American practices but rather to safeguard American health based upon American law.

7. Conclusion: These comments are relatively general in nature and intended as an overview of the Federation's positions on the subject. Nevertheless, the U.S. position absolutely must be one that stresses the importance of consumer choice and access to vitamin and mineral supplements.

Furthermore, you are bound by United States law to reject any lists or limits on vitamins and minerals or other dietary supplements. You cannot commit the United States to being a party to any agreement or protocol that would foist such dietary restrictions upon the United States. I have been disappointed that during the last Codex meeting in Berlin in November 2001, none of the comments or suggestions that I made to you concerning the above were considered or implemented. Rather, the United States delegate's approach was to compromise away our rights and, in doing so, to violate American law. The United States' delegate must re-think its Codex position and follow American law.

Sincerely yours,

Scott C. Tips

SCT:mm
cc: Ms. Maureen Kennedy Salaman, NHF President

NHF NATIONAL
HEALTH
FEDERATION

January 11, 2005

(NHF appeal)
We Need Your Help! Please Read and Act Now!

FAO/WHO Nutrient Risk Assessment Project already exhibits a worrying lack of transparency

An announcement concerning a joint Nutrient Risk Assessment Project was issued earlier this year by the Food and Agriculture Organization of the United Nations (FAO) and the World Health Organization (WHO). The goal of the project is supposedly to define a "scientifically-based and internationally applicable approach for nutrient risk assessment."

One of the key parts of the Project is the convening of an interdisciplinary technical workshop to develop a scientific model for nutrient risk assessment. A "Call for Experts" to take part in this workshop was recently made by the FAO/WHO, and it is anticipated that the workshop will be scheduled for May 2005.

Why is this important?

Because the FAO and the WHO are the joint administrators of the Codex Alimentarius Commission, the results of their nutrient risk assessment project will be hugely influential upon the maximum levels to be set in connection with the Codex Guidelines for Vitamin and Mineral Food Supplements.

However, quite aside from the fact that applying risk assessment models to dietary supplements is both unnecessary and totally inappropriate, the National Health Federation is already very concerned about the transparency of the FAO/WHO Nutrient Risk Assessment Project, as there is currently no indication as to who, specifically, will be making the selection of experts to take part in the workshop.

In order for the Nutrient Risk Assessment Project Workshop to have the confidence of both the public and the scientific community it is clearly essential that the selection of experts to take part in it is conducted with the very highest standards of transparency.

We therefore request that anybody who is concerned about maintaining their access to dietary supplements should email FAO-HQ@fao.org and info@who.int to request that the FAO and WHO make public the names of the person or persons who will be selecting the experts to take part in the workshop to develop a scientific model for nutrient risk assessment.

P.O. Box 688, Monrovia, CA 91017 ~ 1 (626) 357-2181 ~ Fax 1 (626) 303-0642
Website: www.thenhf.com   E-mail: contact-us@thenhf.com

254

Further information about the FAO/WHO Nutrient Risk Assessment Project can be found at http://www.who.int/ipcs/highlights/nutrientraproject/en/

_____

OUR SUGGESTED TEXT FOR YOUR EMAIL TO THE FAO/WHO IS AS FOLLOWS: (COPY AND PASTE THIS INTO YOUR EMAIL PROGRAM)

Dear Sir or Madam:

I am writing to express my concern at the lack of transparency in the selection of experts to participate in the FAO/WHO Nutrient Risk Assessment Workshop. I note from your website that the selection of experts will be made by FAO/WHO, but I have thus far been unable to find any information regarding who, specifically, within the FAO and WHO will be making this selection.

In order for the Nutrient Risk Assessment Project Workshop to have the full confidence of both the public and the scientific community it is clearly essential that the selection of experts to take part in it is conducted with the very highest standards of transparency.

I therefore request that in the interests of transparency you make public the names of the person or persons who will be selecting the experts to take part in this workshop.

Yours sincerely,

P.O. Box 688, Monrovia, CA 91017 ~ 1 (626) 357-2181 ~ Fax 1 (626) 303-0642
Website: www.thenhf.com   E-mail: contact-us@thenhf.com

255

NHF
NATIONAL
HEALTH
FEDERATION

March 29, 2005

Health Federation Comments on Codex Guidelines for Vitamin and Mineral Food Supplements

JOINT FAO/WHO FOOD STANDARDS PROGRAMME

Codex Committee on Nutrition and Foods for Special Dietary Uses

Comments of the National Health Federation on the Draft Guidelines for Vitamin and Mineral Food Supplements at Step 8 of the Procedure (ALINORM 05/28/26 para. 35 and Appendix II):

The National Health Federation considers that the drafting of the Guidelines for Vitamin and Mineral Food Supplements has not been carried out in full accordance with the rules set out in the Codex Procedural Manual (14th edition).

Paragraph (b) (page 57) of the section dealing with DRAWING UP OF CODEX STAN-DARDS (under GUIDELINES ON THE CONDUCT OF MEETINGS OF CODEX COMMITTEES AND AD HOC INTERGOVERNMENTAL TASK FORCES) states that:

.....all standards and related texts should have a preface containing.....a brief description of the scope and purpose(s) of the standard or related text,

This requirement was agreed at the 19th Session of the Codex Committee on General Principles, held in Paris between 17-21 November 2003, and adopted at the 27th Session of the Codex Alimentarius Commission (CAC), held in Geneva between 28th June and 2nd July 2004. The Codex Committee on Nutrition and Foods for Special Dietary Uses (CCNFS-DU) subsequently met in Bonn from 1-5 November 2004 (26th Session) but did not take proper account of this requirement when considering the guidelines, as evidenced by both the CCNFSDU's report of its 26th session and the draft text of the guidelines themselves:

The CCNFSDU's report of its 26th Session gives no indication that the requirement for the preface to contain a description of the purpose of the text was even considered, despite the fact that the matter was raised at this session by the delegations of South Africa, Tanzania and the National Health Federation.

P.O. Box 688, Monrovia, CA 91017 ~ 1 (626) 357-2181 ~ Fax 1 (626) 303-0642
Website: www.thenhf.com   E-mail: contact-us@thenhf.com

Neither the Preamble nor the Scope of the guidelines contain any statement to indicate the purpose(s) of the text. Given therefore that Codex texts have been used as the benchmark in international trade disputes, and moreover that it is expected that they will be used increasingly in this regard, we consider that it is of crucial legal importance that the question "What is the purpose of the guidelines?" should have a clear, easily understandable answer, and moreover that this should be provided in the text.

Bearing the above in mind, the National Health Federation believes that the 28th Session of the Codex Alimentarius Commission has no option but to refer the Guidelines for Vitamin and Mineral Food Supplements back to the CCNFSDU, in accordance with the GUIDE TO THE CONSIDERATION OF STANDARDS AT STEP 8 OF THE PROCEDURE FOR THE ELABORATION OF CODEX STANDARDS INCLUDING CONSIDERATION OF ANY STATEMENTS RELATING TO ECONOMIC IMPACT, as described on pages 26-27 of the Codex Procedural Manual (14th edition). As such, until such time as the CCNFSDU's written comments regarding this matter have been received and considered by the CAC the guidelines should not, and indeed, cannot, be advanced beyond Step 8 of the Procedure.

P.O. Box 688, Monrovia, CA 91017 USA
Tel.: 1 (626) 357-2181
Fax 1 (626) 303-0642
E-mail: contact-us@thenhf.com
Website: www.thenhf.com

P.O. Box 688, Monrovia, CA 91017 ~ 1 (626) 357-2181 ~ Fax 1 (626) 303-0642
Website: www.thenhf.com   E-mail: contact-us@thenhf.com

257

NHF
NATIONAL
HEALTH
FEDERATION

May 5, 200?

NHF Press Release

Codex Breaks its Own Rules!

The Codex Alimentarius Commission, the active arm of the United Nations Food Standards Programme, is currently in the process of completing a controversial global guideline on the manufacture and sale of nutritional supplements. However, the drafting of this text, the Draft Guidelines for Vitamin and Mineral Food Supplements, has not been carried out in accordance with the rules set out in the Codex Procedural Manual (14th edition), and the Guidelines are therefore defective.

Drafted by the Codex Committee on Nutrition and Foods for Special Dietary Uses (CCNFSDU), the Draft Guidelines for Vitamin and Mineral Food Supplements advocate similar restrictions on the sale of nutrients to those contained in the EU Food Supplements Directive, which itself was recently rejected as invalid by Advocate General Geelhoed of the European Court of Justice in Luxembourg.

Specifically, paragraph (b) (page 57) of the Codex Procedural Manual, dealing with DRAWING UP OF CODEX STANDARDS (under GUIDELINES ON THE CONDUCT OF MEETINGS OF CODEX COMMITTEES AND AD HOC INTERGOVERNMENTAL TASK FORCES), states that:

"... all standards and related texts should have a preface containing ... a brief description of the scope and purpose(s) of the standard or related text,"

This requirement was established at the 19th Session of the Codex Committee on General Principles, held in Paris between 17-21 November 2003, and then adopted at the 27th Session of the Codex Alimentarius Commission, held in Geneva between 28th June and 2nd July 2004. The CCNFSDU subsequently met in Bonn from 1-5 November 2004 (26th Session), but did not take proper account of this requirement when considering the guidelines, as evidenced by both the text of the guidelines and the CCNFSDU's report of its 26th session:

1.   **Neither the Preamble nor the Scope of the Guidelines for Vitamin and Mineral Food Supplements contain any statement to indicate the purpose(s) of the text.** Given therefore that Codex texts have been used by the World Trade Organization as the benchmark in international trade disputes, and moreover that it is expected that they will be used increasingly in this regard, it is therefore of crucial legal importance that the question "What is the purpose of the guidelines?" should have a clear, easily understandable answer, and moreover that this should be provided in the text.

P.O. Box 688, Monrovia, CA 91017 ~ 1 (626) 357-2181 ~ Fax 1 (626) 303-0642
Website: www.thenhf.com   E-mail: contact-us@thenhf.com

2.   **The CCNFSDU's Report of its 26th Session gives no indication that the requirement for the preface to contain a description of the purpose of the text was even considered,** despite the fact that the matter was raised at this session by the delegations of South Africa, Tanzania, and the National Health Federation.

With the above in mind, it is now clear that the 28th Session of the Codex Alimentarius Commission that will be meeting in Rome from 4-9 July 2005 has no option but to refer the Guidelines for Vitamin and Mineral Food Supplements back to the CCNFSDU, in accordance with the GUIDE TO THE CONSIDERATION OF STANDARDS AT STEP 8 OF THE PRO-CEDURE FOR THE ELABORATION OF CODEX STANDARDS INCLUDING CONSIDERATION OF ANY STATEMENTS RELATING TO ECONOMIC IMPACT, as described on pages 26-27 of the Codex Procedural Manual (14th edition). As such, until such time as the CCNFSDU's written comments regarding this matter have been received and considered by the Codex Alimentarius Commission, the Codex Guidelines for Vitamin and Mineral Food Supplements should not, and indeed, cannot, be advanced beyond Step 8 of the Procedure. To act other-wise would be for the Commission to violate its own rules of procedure.

For further information contact:

Cheri Tips ct@thenhf.com (North America)
Paul Anthony Taylor paulandpolly@btinternet.com or +44 (0)1325-466361 (Europe).

P.O. Box 688, Monrovia, CA 91017 USA
1 (626) 357-2181
Fax 1 (626) 303-0642
E-mail: contact-us@thenhf.com
Website: www.thenhf.com

P.O. Box 688, Monrovia, CA 91017 ~ 1 (626) 357-2181 ~ Fax 1 (626) 303-0642
Website: www.thenhf.com   E-mail: contact-us@thenhf.com

259

June 2005

NHF Codex Update
by Cheri Tips

What lies ahead for individuals who value their current freedom to choose to consume healthy food, take supplements, and use alternative therapies without government restrictions?

What will become of the manufacturers, retailers of innovative food supplements, and the practitioners that depend upon the availability of these products to keep their patients naturally well?

The year 2005 should be a truly telling year.
There is static in the air concerning these questions, especially amongst health-freedom groups courageously trying to inform the general populace of the truth on these issues but doing so on meager budgets, and with small office support staff. The cavernous pockets of the pharmaceutical companies' media budget enable them to hoodwink consumers by spewing propaganda with their spin of "all is ok, no need to worry" version of the future of vitamins and supplements and to unleash their captive regulators upon an all-too trusting, government-worshiping populace.

Two positives come to mind at this point. First, even though the pharmaceutical companies have deep monetary pockets, and they have contributed enormous amounts of money to federal candidates and lobbying efforts this past year, they are currently on the chopping block concerning the safety of U.S. citizens in regards to the drug supply, with the industry facing new federal scrutiny and possible regulations in the future. Secondly, the internet has become quite a blessing for the health-freedom movement, as we are able to globally network via the world wide web with other health-freedom groups who are fighting the same battles for freedom against pharmaceutical and global harmonization. Thanks to the internet, we do not have to pay postage fees to disseminate our messages to the world and fight the ongoing propaganda.

We will explore the current situation, give you factual information that you may rely upon, discuss what you as an individual may do to assist us, and the important steps involving Codex that the NHF has taken to work to ensure your health freedom.

Codex: Still the Hottest Issue
The National Health Federation is no stranger to Codex, as it is the ONLY health-freedom organization that is officially credentialed as an INGO (International Non-Governmental Organization) by the Codex Alimentarius Commission with the right to attend and speak out at its committee meetings. From a health-freedom standpoint, then, the NHF is the only game in town AT these meetings. For the past five years Scott Tips, NHF board member and legal counsel, has been attending these meetings as our official Codex delegate and reporting back

P.O. Box 688, Monrovia, CA 91017 ~ 1 (626) 357-2181 ~ Fax 1 (626) 303-0642
Website: www.thenhf.com   E-mail: contact-us@thenhf.com

NHF Codex Update
by Cheri Tips

via his articles in Health Freedom News, alerting NHF members and others of the Codex threat. Other NHF board and advisory-board members, Tamara Theresa Mosegaard, Paul Anthony Taylor, and Sepp Hasslberger have also been in attendance at several meetings. Most recently, Paul Anthony Taylor and Scott Tips were present at the Codex Committee General Principles Meeting held in Paris, France on April 11-15th, 2005. No stone is left unturned by the NHF when it comes to Codex, and our information relating to Codex is highly credible.

Unfortunately, there is much misinformation circulating regarding Codex. Some individuals have not thoroughly researched all data on this convoluted issue, and other false information is probably intentionally being sent to dupe the reader into comfortable ignorance of the subject in an attempt by pharma-backed groups whose goal is to ultimately force supplements into being categorized as drugs via Codex and global harmonization. This spin is flagrantly being cast out to the unsuspecting by groups such as the Council for Responsible Nutrition (CRN), another group that has non-governmental status at the Codex meetings, and even by the National Nutritional Foods Association (NNFA), who represent retailers, manufacturers, and distributors of health and sports nutrition foods. Their tactics present the NHF and other health-freedom groups with an even more uphill battle as we waste time countering their high- priced PR firm sendouts to the unknowing. Grassroots health-freedom groups are popping up like flowers after a spring rain. We feel, though, the more the merrier as long as they are true to their word and not pharmaceutical-company backed, fronting as our ally.

The Federation has been watching and acting upon the Codex issue for many years, attending its meetings, and speaking out at the Committee meetings for all health-freedom advocates for half a decade. Our members are quite familiar with the issue.

In November 2004, at the Bonn, Germany Codex Committee on Nutrition and Foods for Special Dietary Uses (the committee which first drafted the Codex Draft Guidelines for Vitamin and Food Supplements), the NHF was represented by delegates Scott Tips, Paul Anthony Taylor, and Sepp Hasslberger. During this meeting the National Health Federation brought up the issue of the Committee's proposed adoption of the draft Guidelines at Step 8 and the fact that the drafting of those Guidelines had not been carried out in full accordance with the rules set out in the Codex Procedural Manual (14th edition). Once addressed, there was no action taken by the Committee.

With the FAO (Food and Agricultural Organization of the United Nations) and WHO (World Health Organization) being joint administrators of the Codex Alimentarius Committee, the NHF is persevering in its efforts to be heard on this violation of policy. In late March, our organization submitted a formal paper (see http://www.thenhf.com/codex_37.htm) to the Codex

P.O. Box 688, Monrovia, CA 91017 ~ 1 (626) 357-2181 ~ Fax 1 (626) 303-0642
Website: www.thenhf.com   E-mail: contact-us@thenhf.com

261

Alimentarius Commission for its consideration at the upcoming meeting in Rome, Italy. Receipt of this paper has been confirmed and both Scott Tips and Paul Anthony Taylor will be attending this meeting, which will occur on July 4-9, 2005. We expect quite a fight on this issue.

Because of the seriousness of this situation the NHF decided to go public with the matter by issuing a press release on May 5th, 2005, to bring this to the attention of the widest possible audience (see http://www.thenhf.com/codex_may_2005_nhf_press_release.htm).

In January 2005, on another issue that would greatly affect supplements, the NHF addressed concern over the transparency of a workshop that FAO and WHO were announcing to define a "scientifically-based and internationally applicable approach for nutrient risk assessment." Their joint project was calling for "experts" to take part in the May 2005 workshop with the goal being to develop a scientific model for nutrient risk assessment. Their choice of experts could greatly affect the maximum levels that would be set, thereby influencing Codex Guidelines for Vitamin and Mineral Food Supplements. However, because there was no indication as to who, specifically, would be making the selection of experts to take part in the workshop, the NHF requested that the FAO and WHO make public the names of the person or persons who would be selecting the experts to take part in it (see http://www.thenhf.com/codex_30.htm). As regular readers of this newsletter will know, a worrying lack of transparency of this sort is all too common within the Codex, FAO, and WHO systems.

Codex Coalition for Health Freedom
A meeting was organized by Breena Hill and Cheryl Dicks of the American Association of Health Freedom and held April 22nd and 23rd, 2005 in Virginia to officially form a U.S. Codex Coalition. The AAHF did a very professional job with the meeting and deserve immense credit for its efforts. The coalition group decided to call itself the Coalition for Health Freedom, and will be an umbrella group of health-freedom organizations united to oppose the current direction of Codex to severely restrict vitamins and minerals throughout the world. Secondarily, the group hopes to directly counter the media spin that has begun to circulate with its false message of "all is well." Top Codex experts made presentations and specific lobbying and strategy efforts were discussed. The National Health Federation was represented by Scott Tips, with Paul Anthony Taylor and NHF lobbyist, Lee Bechtel, also in attendance. Members of Congress have been sent a survey form to gain an understanding of what they really know about the Codex agenda.

How can our members and readers assist in efforts against the corrupt Codex process?
First, you must educate yourself with factual information. Go to our website www.thenhf.com. Most important to this subject are our pages entitled Codex, EU Issues, Government Affairs (Federal), and the Articles page. Once you have a true understanding of the subject, inform others, as many people know nothing of Codex and its consequences. We would like Codex to become a household word as mainstream media is keeping the lid on it.

P.O. Box 688, Monrovia, CA 91017 ~ 1 (626) 357-2181 ~ Fax 1 (626) 303-0642
Website: www.thenhf.com   E-mail: contact-us@thenhf.com

262

NHF Codex Update
by Cheri Tips

Re: Recent NHF Codex Press Release
(See http://www.thenhf.com/codex_may_2005_nhf_press_release.htm)

Given the clear intent of the Codex Alimentarius Commission to flout its own procedural rules, we feel that we are entirely justified in wanting to bring this matter to as wide an audience as possible in the run up to the Commission's next meeting which will be taking place in Rome in early July. It is at this meeting that the Commission will be attempting to adopt the Guidelines for Vitamin and Mineral Food Supplements as a newly agreed global standard, and if they are successful our future health freedoms here in the United States, and indeed everywhere else in the world, will be very much at risk.

You can greatly assist us in our efforts by persistently bringing this matter to the attention of your Congressmen and Senators, as a first step towards (hopefully) encouraging the US FDA delegation to vote in Rome in favor of returning the Guidelines to Bonn for further consideration by the Codex Committee on Nutrition and Foods for Special Dietary Uses at their next meeting in November 2005.

The sad aspect of all this of course is that we know only too well that the US FDA is not on our side, as its website clearly demonstrates that the agency is pro-harmonization. The one way that we can possibly change their collective minds therefore is to collectively put pressure on them through our legislators. The NHF membership has a well-known history of positive impact when they rally to a cause and inundate legislators with their calls and handwritten personal letters on a topic.

The NHF is preparing for the next meeting of Codex in Rome, Italy, July 2005. The Commission will be attempting to adopt the Guidelines for Vitamin and Mineral Food Supplements to become a global standard. This is an extremely dangerous time for health-freedom proponents all over the world.

P.O. Box 688, Monrovia, CA 91017 ~ 1 (626) 357-2181 ~ Fax 1 (626) 303-0642
Website: www.thenhf.com   E-mail: contact-us@thenhf.com

October 28, 2006

National Health Federation Heads to Codex Meeting in Thailand

The National Health Federation delegation for the Codex Committee on Nutrition and Foods for Special Dietary Uses (28th Session), held in Chiang Mai, Thailand on October 30 - November 3, 2006, will be Ingrid Franzon (Sweden), as the Head of the Delegation, assisted by Dr. Robert Verkerk (UK) and Dr. Wong Ang Peng (Malaysia).

P.O. Box 688, Monrovia, CA 91017 ~ 1 (626) 357-2181 ~ Fax 1 (626) 303-0642
Website: www.thenhf.com   E-mail: contact-us@thenhf.com

Transcript of the National Health Federation Statement at Codex

by Carolyn Dean, M.D., NHF, USA & Friends of Freedom International
(FOFI, Canada)

July 4, 2005

Scott Tips of the National Health Federation was recognized by the chair. The following is a transcription of Scott Tips' statement at Codex regarding the vitamin and mineral guidelines.

Thank you Mr. Chairman. The NHF is a world wide consumer organization. We compliment you on your rapidity with which you have adopted many draft guidelines here today. But this is one that should not be rushed and should not be approved. It should not be rushed in the same way as the others.

I encourage you to read the document that is being distributed to you right now: for these defective guidelines are incomplete and may not be adopted because, first of all, they contain no statement of purpose in the preface, which is contrary to our own rules of procedure.

What are they there for if we do not follow them? We cannot do that; they have to be sent back to Bonn for redrafting. Second, they don't define what vitamins and minerals are. The FAO has admitted that they cannot provide us with a list of the vitamins and minerals that are supposed to be defined in this document. You are trying to pass a document that is not complete or defined.

Third, Mr. Chairman you are quite correct when you said that the Chinese comments are subtantive and as the Columbian delegate pointed out his comments are substantive too. And, page 27 of the Codex Procedural Manual says that if an amendment is ruled as substantive, it shall be referred back to the Committee. The Guideline must, therefore, be sent back to Committee. Thank you Mr Chairman.

(Friends of Freedom International / http://www.friendsoffreedom.org)

NHF NATIONAL HEALTH FEDERATION

Joint FAO? WHO Food Standards Programme
Codex Committee on Nutrition and Foods for
Special Dietary Uses

**Comments of the National Health Federation on the Draft
Guidelines for Vitamin and Mineral Food Supplements at Step 8 of
the Procedure (ALINORM 05/28/26 para. 35 and Appendix II):**

The National Health Federation considers that the drafting of the
Guidelines for Vitamin and Mineral Food Supplements has not
been carried out in full accordance with the rules set out in the
Codex Procedural Manual (14th edition).

Paragraph (b) (page 57) of the section dealing with DRAW-
ING UP OF CODEX STANDARDS (under GUIDELINES ON
THE CONDUCT OF MEETINGS OF CODEX COMMITTEES
AND AD HOC INTERGOVERNMENTAL TASK FORCES)
states that:

> .....all standards and related texts should have a
> preface containing.....a brief description of the
> scope and purpose(s) of the standard or related text,

This requirement was agreed at the 19th Session of the Codex
Committee on General Principles, held in Paris between 17-21
November 2003, and adopted at the 27th Session of the Codex
Alimentarius Commission (CAC), held in Geneva between 28th
June and 2nd July 2004. The Codex Committee on Nutrition and
Foods for Special Dietary Uses (CCNFSDU) subsequently met in
Bonn from 1-5 November 2004 (26th Session) but did not take
proper account of this requirement when considering the guide-
lines, as evidenced by both the CCNFSDU's report of its 26th ses-
sion and the draft text of the guidelines themselves:

P.O. Box 688, Monrovia, CA 91017 ~ 1 (626) 357-2181 ~ Fax 1 (626) 303-0642
Website: www.thenhf.com   E-mail: contact-us@thenhf.com

266

1. The CCNFSDU's report of its 26th Session gives no indication that the requirement for the preface to contain a description of the purpose of the text was even considered, despite the fact that the matter was raised at this session by the delegations of South Africa, Tanzania and the National Health Federation.

2. Neither the Preamble nor the Scope of the guidelines contain any statement to indicate the purpose(s) of the text. Given therefore that Codex texts have been used as the benchmark in international trade disputes, and moreover that it is expected that they will be used increasingly in this regard, we consider that it is of crucial legal importance that the question "What is the purpose of the guidelines?" should have a clear, easily understandable answer, and moreover that this should be provided in the text.

Bearing the above in mind, the National Health Federation believes that the 28th Session of the Codex Alimentarius Commission has no option but to refer the Guidelines for Vitamin and Mineral Food Supplements back to the CCNFSDU, in accordance with the GUIDE TO THE CONSIDERATION OF STANDARDS AT STEP 8 OF THE PROCEDURE FOR THE ELABORATION OF CODEX STANDARDS INCLUDING CONSIDERATION OF ANY STATEMENTS RELATING TO ECONOMIC IMPACT, as described on pages 26-27 of the Codex Procedural Manual (14th edition). As such, until such time as the CCNFSDU's written comments regarding this matter have been received and considered by the CAC the guidelines should not, and indeed, cannot, be advanced beyond Step 8 of the Procedure.

P.O. Box 688, Monrovia, CA 91017 ~ 1 (626) 357-2181 ~ Fax 1 (626) 303-0642
Website: www.thenhf.com   E-mail: contact-us@thenhf.com

INDEX

AAHF 262

Alliance for Natural Health ix, 131, 157, 166, 168, 181, 187

American Holistic Health Association ix, 55, 75, 85, 102, 129, 230, 232

ANH 131, 132, 167, 169

Booyzen, Antoinette vi, x, 74, 82, 111, 185, 192, 115, 114

CAFTA vii, 222-224

CCFL 107, 109, 176, 191-194, 204

CCNFSDU iv, v, vi, ix, x, xii, 15, 21-22, 55-57, 62, 85-87, 92-93, 107, 109-111, 114-115, 119-120, 138-139, 143-148, 150-154, 180, 182-183, 185, 187, 197-201, 224-225, 249, 250, 256-259, 266-167

Codex Alimentarius Commission iv, vi, x, xii, xiv, 9, 15-16, 21, 25. 38, 41, 47, 61, 93, 95, 100, 102-103, 105, 106, 109, 119-124, 127, 140, 143, 146, 154, 155-156, 161, 176, 184, 191, 216, 222, 231, 246-247, 249, 254, 256-259, 258, 259, 260-261, 266-267

Council for Responsible Nutrition x, 50, 77, 83, 90. 98, 113, 220, 261

CRN x, 12, 50, 77, 83, 90, 98, 113, 220, 261

Dean, Carolyn ix, 96, 161, 265

Dr. Rath Foundation vii, 65, 162, 231,

DSHEA viii, 38-39

Dybring, Alex 17, 227

European Union vi, xi, 10, 15, 43, 57, 60, 68-69, 75-76, 80, 87, 97, 99-101, 103, 130, 137, 144, 156, 166, 174, 200, 214, 222, 227

Food and Agriculture Organization iv, xiv, 15, 18, 21, 25, 65, 75, 95, 122, 156, 171, 185, 191, 198

Food and Drug Administration v, 10, 32, 42, 75, 206, 213-214, 218, 251, 253

Food Supplements Directive vi, xv, 100, 130, 137-138, 156, 158, 166, 169, 174, 258

Foundation for Health Research xi, 230

Franzon, Ingrid ix, 197, 230, 264

FTAA 224

GATT 9, 17, 21, 221

Gormley, James vii

Grossklaus, Dr. Rolf ii, vi, 32, 48, 77, 80, 86, 120, 164, 171, 173-175, 183, 225

Hammell, John vi, 209, 228

Harris, Suzanne vi

Hasslberger, Sepp vi, vii, 1, 65, 96, 105, 127, 131, 161, 166, 179, 114, 228, 261

Hathcock, John vii, 133

Health Freedom News 47, 95, 109, 161, 183, 191, 197, 231, 261,

IADSA 81, 90, 91, 100, 165, 220

IAHF vi, 210, 216, 228,

La Leva vii, 8, 161, 228

INDEX

MayDay vii, 15-17, 25, 28, 29, 80, 96, 161, 227, 229

Miller, Diane vii, 162

Miller, Kevin vii, 187

Mathioudakis, Basil viii, 95, 120, 130, 179,

Mosegaard, Tamara Thérèsa 15, 17, 25, 80, 96, 161, 203

NAFTA v, 9, 209, 210, 216, 222, 264

National Health Federation vii, iv, xiv, xv, 16, 31, 48, 60, 74, 80, 87, 90,96, 121, 127, 153, 161, 173, 179, 180, 182-183, 191, 195, 197, 203, 222, 225, 230, 231, 249-250, 252, 254, 256-257, 259-262, 264-267

Negus, Susan vii, 41, 230

NHF 60, 74-76, 80-81, 83, 87, 90-92, 97-103,111, 121, 123, 127, 161-164, 173, 180-185, 192-195, 197, 199-201, 203-205, 207-208, 114-115, 224-225, 227, 229, 231, 232, 253-254, 257-263, 265-267

NLEA 212, 260

North American Union v, 209-211, 216

Rath, Dr. Mathias vii, 65, 67, 119, 162, 231

Risk analysis ii. vii, 50, 67, 122, 128, 175, 177, 182, 186-187

Risk assessment viii, 33-34, 50-53, 59, 60-61, 76, 83-84, 90, 101, 120, 122-123, 128, 131-136, 144, 151-153, 156, 166, 175, 180-181, 185-187, 197-198-200, 205, 215, 222, 244-45, 247, 253-255, 262

Salaman, Maureen Kennedy xii, xv, 230, 253

Sanitary and PhytoSanitary Agreement 221

Taylor, Paul Anthony vii, 80, 96, 109, 119, 161, 171, 181, 183, 114-115, 231, 259, 261, 262

Technical Barriers to Trade (TBT) v, 223

Tips, Cheri 182, 259, 260-263

Tips, Scott ix, xiv, 30, 31, 37, 47, 73, 79, 95, 113, 114-115, 127, 161, 179-180, 183, 191, 205, 217, 231, 253, 260-262, 265

Turner, James viii

Verkerk, Robert vii 131, 169, 181, 183, 187, 197, 264

Walter, Suzan vii, 55, 75, 85, 102, 129, 137, 143, 155, 232

We Become Silent viii, 187

Whole Foods Magazine 21, 31, 37, 43, 47, 73, 79, 161, 167, 232

World Health Organization ii, xi, 15, 18, 21, 25, 79, 87, 95, 122, 139, 156, 173, 180, 185, 191, 198, 244-245, 254, 261

World Trade Organization ii, v, 10, 17, 37-38, 43, 48, 61, 79, 85, 102, 129, 138, 145, 156, 166, 182, 221, 232, 258

Yetley, Dr. Elizabeth ii, vi, 32, 49, 74, 250